TODAY'S INFORMATION
FOR TOMORROW'S PRODUCTS
an Operations Research Approach

Books by George K. Chacko

THE MAR THOMA SYRIAN LITURGY
(*A Translation into English,* 1956)

THE MAR THOMA SYRIAN CHURCH ORDER OF HOLY
MATRIMONY
(*A Translation into English,* 1957)

INDIA: TOWARD AN UNDERSTANDING, 1959

INTERNATIONAL TRADE ASPECTS OF INDIAN BURLAP:
AN ECONOMETRIC STUDY, 1961

TODAY'S INFORMATION FOR TOMORROW'S PRODUCTS — An
Operations Research Approach, 1966

today's

information

for

tomorrow's

products

an operations
research approach

by
george k. chacko

1966
THOMPSON BOOK COMPANY
Washington, D. C.
•

THOMPSON BOOK COMPANY
383 National Press Building
Washington, D. C. 20004

Library of Congress catalog number: 66-23480

Printed in the United States of America

Dedicated affectionately to our first-born

RAJAH

Who, with one male shout, conceptually transformed us, an
international couple, into a United Nations family

CONTENTS

FOREWORD

An essential feature of operations research is complexity. Furthermore, it is complexity not only in the traditional forms of the world of engineering and science, but a fuzzy complexity in the twilight zone between the social and the physical sciences. In order to treat these problems in a systematic and meaningful fashion, a firm conceptual basis is required. The conceptual basis is that of a philosophy of the rational approach to problem-solving. Such an approach cannot be the consequence of an armchair philosophy. On the contrary, it must be a synthesis of experience and theory.

Over time a cadre of people trained in application of the scientific method to the management of both governmental and industrial systems has developed. George Chacko is one of these. It is a pleasure to welcome his book describing his ideas and theories and to call it to the attention of those who feel, as I do, that successful operations of the major systems of our society represents a series of challenges of the highest order.

RICHARD BELLMAN
University of Southern California

PREFACE

This work deals with operations research, rather than with an assortment of mathematical techniques. It is concerned with strategies of policy rather than with techniques of suboptimization. It develops an integrated way of looking at widely varying entities which enter into making decisions today for tomorrow's products — consumer products, durable goods, weapons systems, space technology, and many types of services. Illustrations are drawn from real life. Information systems are set up which incorporate accepted classifications such as the Standard Industrial Classification System (SIC).

Part I surveys the perspective of operations research in practical situations, leading to the development of a consistent set of objectives whether for corporations, governments, military establishments, or various kinds of institutions. The operational levels of decisions are identified and related to the overall objectives, and a system of penalties for failing to achieve different objectives is worked out.

Part II develops feasibility considerations from a technological point of view which enter into the pursuit of the objectives covered in Part I. These considerations are as pertinent to space travel as to "deheadache" remedies — hypothetical pills designed not to cure but to prevent headaches. Again, the management decisions required to nurture ideas into outputs are similar in nature whether the orientation is to problems in outer space or to aches and pains in the body.

Part III considers the ordering of information from within and from without, and the drawing of implications from such information for the scrutiny of the decision-makers. Two new concepts have been developed here: Periodic Table of Product Diversification (PTPD), which provides new insights into the *potential* outputs, and Central Intelligence Retrieval System (CIRS), which provides new insights into *present* outputs.

Part IV discusses the philosophy of information usage, presenting still another new concept, that of Concomitant Coalitions — and explores the implications of this concept for committing today's resources to tomorrow's hopes.

This work, which utilizes only a bare minimum of mathematics, should be of interest to readers in many different areas of management research and operations as well as to graduate and undergraduate students in these fields. To the management decision-maker it sets forth the reasoning and real-life applications which must underlie his decisions. To the policy advisor it provides the ordering of information and the interrelationships among the different types of information vis-à-vis the objectives of the entity. To the systems analyst it offers the profile of different information systems, the constituent elements, and the type of computations required. And to the operations research worker it outlines the creative contributions of his chosen field not in terms of suboptimization techniques but in the broader aspects of policy strategies.

Bethesda, Md.   GEORGE K. CHACKO
June, 1966

TODAY'S INFORMATION
FOR TOMORROW'S PRODUCTS

an Operations Research Approach

AT STAKE—SURVIVAL

The commitment of today's resources to tomorrow's hopes is vital not only to the race for space but also for the very survival of our way of life. Sputnik I which shot into space ushered in a new era and served to highlight the alternate assumptions underlying the allocation of resources and the direction of research in the United States and the U.S.S.R. The series of individual decisions leading to the successful launching of satellites can be construed to have flown from strategy decisions pertaining to space; or in the absence of such strategies decided upon by design, the constituent decisions may be construed to have issued from such strategies by default. These strategies are indispensable to the conquest of space; they are indispensable to the furtherance of life on this planet. Their concern is with anticipation and response: how, in the face of unparalleled dimensions

1

unfolding in the unborn tomorrows, the decision is made today in the light of yesterday's information to reach out to the future.

Mankind's achievements have been due in large part to an ability to cope with change. Expanding populations, social and political upheavals, and a scientific revolution have made it imperative for our society to find solutions to growing and increasingly complex problems with as little delay as possible. . . .

It is to managers who grow with the needs and resources of their times that we must continue to look for the new ideas and their implementation to meet the challenges of the future.[1]

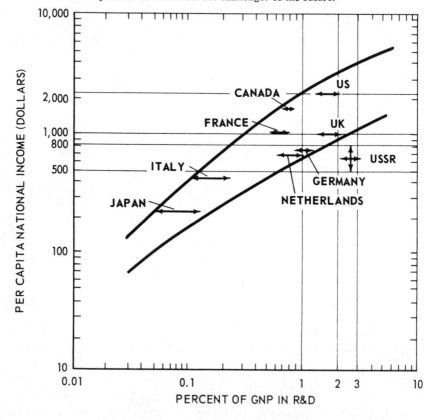

SOURCE: Ellis A. Johnson, "The Crisis in Science and Technology and Its Effect on Military Development," *Operations Research*, January–February, 1958, page 13

Figure 1. PER CAPITA NATIONAL INCOME AND RESEARCH AND DEVELOPMENT EXPENDITURES.

[1] John F. Kennedy, Diamond Jubilee Greetings to The Society for Advancement of Management, August 19, 1963.

NATIONAL R&D EXPENDITURES

The national investment to "cope with change" and "to meet the challenges of the future" is sizable. The national expenditure for all research and development programs in 1962 reached $15 billion, an increase of $1 billion over the previous year, and according to the best estimates available, the total outlays for all research and development activities in 1966 are expected to exceed $21 billion.

We see in Figure 1 the percentage of Gross National Product (GNP) spent on Research and Development (R&D) by different countries and their respective national incomes expressed in U.S. dollars. Two freehand curves are drawn to envelop the lower and upper bounds of the estimated fraction of GNP. It is seen that the United States, with a per capita income of over $2,000, spent approximately 2 percent of GNP, while the United Kingdom, with half the U.S. per capita income, spent the same percentage of its GNP on R&D. The U.S.S.R., with per capita income one-fourth to one-third that of the U.S.A., or $500–$800, spent a higher fraction, perhaps 150 percent of the U.S. percentage on R&D.*

What considerations govern the allocation of funds to and in R&D?

"OFFENSIVE" AND "DEFENSIVE" RESEARCH

The National Science Foundation sponsored a study of the allocation of R&D expenditures, which said in part:

> The management of research-oriented industrial organizations is concerned with allocating some of its available funds to and within R&D activities. . . .
> In the course of this study, we found that the companies involved — and we have reason to believe that most companies — do not keep R&D records in such a way as to yield accurate data on past expenditures classified in this way [to answer budgeting questions: how much to allocate to R&D over a planning period (e.g., one year?); how to divide these funds between types of R&D?]. Consequently we search for an alternative classification that would be both useful and feasible. The most suitable classification we found was: (a) *New product* or process research: *offensive* research (b) *Existing* product or process research: improvement or *defensive* research. . . .
> Since R&D can be classified as either offensive or defensive,

---

*A subsequent study by Herbert K. Weiss reported in *Management Science* (vol. 11, no. 3, January, 1965, pp. 368-394) finds agreement with Ellis Johnsons empirical expression $P_c = 1300\ R^{2/3}$ where P_c is per capita national income and R is research and development as percentage of GNP (p.388).

the sum of the allocations to these two classes is the total R&D
budget. We shall refer to this as the *general* budgeting problem.
The *special* budgeting problem [becomes]: how much to allocate
to specific R&D projects?[2]

"Existing product" is an identifiable entity, but how about "new
product?" The "newness" which distinguishes it from the "existing"
product has to be *operationally* specified. It would not be adequate simply
to legislate for the "new product": creativity rarely flows at command. Even
if the "new product" were suddenly to materialize one bright morning, how
in fact would it be recognized as the long-awaited "new product"? In the
meantime, how may signposts be devised and recognized along the
uncertain path toward the unknown "new product"?

OUTLINE OF THIS WORK

I: PERSPECTIVE OF ORGANISM

In committing today's resources to tomorrow's hopes, the outcome
is anything but certain. The challenges of the environment are sought to be
met by means of the different choices offered by alternate solutions.
"Offensive" and "defensive" research allocations may be looked upon as
two sets — even two generic sets — of alternative solutions to meet the
challenges of the market. However, the challenges of the environment,
represented by the demands of the market, are neither readily nor fully
enumerated; and in the light of the explosive growth of human knowledge,
the choices of solutions offered are even less readily or fully enumerated.
The *content* of the challenges of the environment as well as the choices of
solutions being thus imperfectly known, if not only imperfectly knowable,
the *context* of the decision-making assumes undeniable importance. This
context is discussed in Part I, "Perspective of Organism."

The decision-affecting and decision-affected entities are *organisms*.
The term "organism" denotes the fact that the constituents are animate,
that they interact, that their dynamic interrelationships tend to generate
intangibles which can sometimes make the whole considerably larger or
considerably smaller than the sum of its parts. Thus, a well-motivated team
of workers produces much more than the arithmetic sum of their individual
capabilities, measured in common units like salaries, years of training and
experience, etc., whereas a poorly motivated team produces much less than
their individual capabilities.

---

[2] Case Institute, "Summary of Case Institute Report for National Science
Foundation," 1959, pp. 3-4.

Organismic viewpoint underlies operations research. It is the art of applying the scientific method to executive-type decision problems. It is also the practice of translating progressively what-can-be into what-is in industrial, commercial, military, and/or institutional environments. Thus operations research is indispensable to identify the potentials of alternate solutions to meet the challenges of the environment as well as to implement them.

Feasibility is a prerequisite to implementation.

If the "new product" were technologically impossible, not only in the light of the present but also the potential, then no amount of R&D allocations would deliver the goods. Even if it is technically feasible to make the product — one can in fact make a silk purse out of a sow's ear — the product has still to be marketable before R&D expenditures in behalf of the technologically feasible product will be authorized by a profit-making entity.

II: PROFILE OF POTENTIAL

In Part II, Profile of Potential, we discuss the technological feasibility of outputs. What "products" are technically feasible? A similar question was posed in the 1870's: What "elements" are structurally feasible? The ingenuity and the skill in formulating the periodic law as a means of discovering elements which would satisfy certain properties solely by reason of structural arrangement is explored with a view to find an answer to the question: What products are technically feasible? The new concepts of "Technometric Structure," "Dimensions of Discovery," and "Axis of Discovery and Locus of Realization" are applied to explain the transformation of industry: from fresh fruit to frozen foods, and from aircraft to aerospace; and to derive guidelines for research and development allocations, whether for headache remedies or for interstellar travels.

Once the new idea is demonstrated to be technically feasible by actual demonstration, or by conceptual establishment of the idea in a class of realizable ideas, there is a perilous journey ahead for the transformation of the idea into output via management decisions. The actualization of ideas and decisiveness of decisions are followed on the one hand, from idea to development, development to prototype, and from prototype to output; and the management activity horizon and the degree of data-processing sophistication on the other. Getting down to cases, as it were, from (a) the discussion of the external factors of technological feasibility and the axis of discovery and (b) the internal factors of long-range planning and organismic decision-making, we ask in Part III, Processing of Information, How can the organism process current information in order to predict potential products?

III: PROCESSING OF INFORMATION

An output is intended to satisfy at least one want, and its ability to satisfy the want (its S-Index) is evaluated by the consumer in terms of the vital nature of the want satisfied (its V-Index). Within the framework of the new Periodic Table of Product Diversification (PTPD), the elements of strength and weakness of the component markets of each output are highlighted, as well as the stage of its growth, so that (1) the predominant sales performance of a few groups of products in favorable growth stage does not give the impression of innate strength for the entire portfolio of products, and (2) advantage can be taken of the groundwork laid with respect to the V-Index by Output 1 to introduce another, a complementary product 2.

The philosophy of the Periodic Table of Product Diversification is that even as the chemical Periodic Table indicated, by its very *structure,* missing elements, so also the elements of strength and weakness of the component market of each output (product), as well as the life-cycle stage of the product can suggest (a) the types of products which need be introduced (b) at specific periods of time in the future (c) to take the place of other products expected to decline by that time.

The Central Intelligence Retrieval System (CIRS) is developed to process information to aid the allocation of resources to research and development. Its philosophy is that apparently formless masses of *input,* comprising published and unpublished reports, government statistics, and hopeful estimates, facts of life and figments of imagination, can be transformed into the *output* of ordered sets of desired alternatives at the disposal of the organism, providing insights into interrelationships which are unavailable from the bits and pieces of data, or even from an assemblage of them, without planned provision for making intelligence out of information. PTPD can suggest the direction in which the developments of the output of the organism should take place, in the light of the best understanding of its own contemporary performance. CIRS, on the other hand, indicates what particular lines of activity are most desirable for the organism, in the light of the performance of other organisms. While these are broad categorizations of the role of PTPD and CIRS, the lines are crossed over, PTPD providing insights into the potential outputs, and CIRS providing insights into present outputs.

IV: PHILOSOPHY OF ALLOCATION

How should information be converted into insight, and insight into decisions of allocations? The processes are governed by what may be considered the philosophy of information usage. This is the subject of Part IV, Philosophy of Allocation.

The innovation profile is constructed on the basis of quantum jumps in the behavioral properties of resources of the organism, the tempo of innovation of the organism, and the tempo of innovation of the competition. The intent here is to change, and, hopefully, to change for the better. Change involves replacement of the past by the present, and the present by the future. The judicious allocation of resources for research and development are predicated on the premise that dimensions of discovery and tempo of innovation can be engineered to yield a suitable new lift to the output portfolio of the organism.

But there is an *escalatory* procedure underneath the improvements and innovations in outputs. If one walks up an escalator, the immediately obvious progress can be stated in terms of the steps climbed. But even as the person is climbing the steps, the escalator itself is moving in the same direction. Therefore, using the handrails of the escalator as the frame of reference, the escalatory motion accentuates the ambulatory motion of the person.

Something like this takes place in the process of discovery associated with research efforts. The dimensions of discovery and the tempo of innovation are somewhat like the steps on the escalator which are directly visible, and which are climbed step-by-step. However, the very process of step-by-step climbing of making improvements in the performance of current properties of resources, or of making innovations, leads to a deeper understanding of the appropriate underlying structure of matter, or its conversion into energy. Such basic understandings contribute, on occasion, to an altogether radical departure in the step-by-step climbing with respect to behavioral properties of resources. Even as the effect of escalatory movement is not apparent until the top of the stairs is reached, so also the effect of radical departures that have been generated by the escalatory movement of fundamental understanding do not come to ready recognition except at discrete time intervals. Unlike the escalator, however, the specific instant at which the escalatory movement will be clearly recognized is *not* predetermined. In terms of the calendar, it may be days, months, weeks, or years before such a discovery is made — with reverberations in all directions.

In other words, current research is digging its own grave. The very

furtherance of understanding it accomplishes almost insures that the accomplishments themselves will be supplanted by efforts to generate further
accomplishments. Thus the present research efforts (a) contain the seeds of
future research efforts (b) so that the current research efforts may be considered at work to obliterate themselves: a game in which (a) plays
AGAINST (b) and simultaneously *WITH* (b) against itself, (a).

The concept of CONCOMITANT COALITIONS is developed as
the analytical framework of allocation of resources to research and development. Its philosophy is a view of the relationship between the present
and the future which underscores the essential, and perpetual, conflict inherent in the very fact of dichotomy of the present and the future. Concomitant Coalition develops the analytical viewpoint that in the present
research efforts (a) themselves are contained the seeds of future efforts
(b), so that the current research efforts may be considered to obliterate
themselves: a game in which (a) plays *AGAINST* (b) and simultaneously
with (b) against itself, (a).

PART I

PERSPECTIVE OF ORGANISM

CHAPTER ONE

ORIENTATION TO OPERATIONS RESEARCH

THE DUAL ASPECT OF ART [1]

What do you see?
A young lady?
An old lady?
Or both?

---

[1] From C. Spearman, *Creative Mind*, D. Appleton-Century Co., Inc.

What you see is a specific interpretation of the given lines, of the light and shadow, in this picture. The specific combination that you have selected reflects the way you relate the drawing to yourself. Bishop Berkeley said sometime ago: *"existens percipere"* — existence is perception. Thus, your particular interpretation is an attribute of your very existence itself.

Why is it that your interpretation of this particular drawing is similar to, or different from, that of others who also look at the same drawing? Hadley Cantril observes:

> From the vast array of happenings going on around us, we select for *at*tention those related to our *in*tention. We become aware of what we sense is probably important for us to be aware of. The process of perceiving is the process of guessing or betting on what our behaviour should be to further our purposes and to have the kind of experience we intend to have. . . .
>
> The process of perceiving the world around us, our orienting ourselves so that we can act effectively to carry out our purposes is a never-ending process of prediction which we make on the basis of faith in the face of uncertainties. Hence, our reality world must undergo constant revision as we experience the inadequacies of the up-to-the-now assumptions we bring to the variety of new and different occasions of living. What we apparently do is to create for ourselves reality worlds which will more effectively further our basic purposes as human beings. And we do this most efficiently only if we use the value satisfaction rather than consistency as our guiding standard for revision.[2]

Your interpretation of the particular drawing is thus a function of your reality world, as Cantril calls it. Even as certain specific ingredients of this reality world made possible your interpretation, different professions require different reality worlds of their memberships, the objective of which is perception of a particular kind.

The operations research professional is a perceptive individual who has specific talents and skills. The specific talents include the clear ability to see the organism as a whole, whether the organism is an industry, a business firm, a military installation, an aerospace complex, or any other entity involved more or less with executive-type decision-making. The specific skills include the ability to conceptualize problems in given situations, and in most instances, to express them in mathematical form which will reflect reality closely, and provide workable models thereof.

---

[2] Hadley Cantril, *The Politics of Despair* (New York: Basic Books, Inc., 1958), pp. 14, 25.

ANALOGY OF MEDICAL DOCTOR

The functioning of the operations research professional seems to be analogous to that of a medical doctor. The doctor works with the symptoms. Out of the given symptoms he constructs diseases. In fact, he constructs not diseases but hypotheses of diseases. On the strength of his hypothesis he prescribes remedies, knowing full well that wrong diagnosis can be serious, even fatal. The doctor's ability to construct diseases out of symptoms is what distinguishes him from a mere dispenser of medicine.

The practice of medicine is a profession; so is the practice of operations research. Parsons defines profession as:

A category of occupational role which is organized about the mastery of and fiduciary responsibility for any important segment of society's cultured tradition including responsibility for its perpetuation *and* for its further development.[3]

What segment of society's "cultured tradition" is the domain of operations research? A parallel will be helpful here.

According to the best-known medical papyrus, the early Egyptian practice of medicine was characterized by "some skill in surgery and a very little knowledge of anatomy."[4] Two major factors helped alter the state of the art: one, the devastation caused by the epidemics of the sixteenth century; and two, the "advent of a school of art which studied the human body in detail, and therefore, demanded a knowledge of human anatomy. The main exponent of this method on the scientific as well as the artistic side was Leonardo da Vinci (1452-1518)."[5]

Even as the preservation of human life is the "cultured tradition" of the medical profession, the translation of what-ought-to-be into what-is, in management of resources via managerial decision-making, is the "cultured tradition" of operations research profession.

However, there are at least three differences between the practice of medicine and the practice of operations research.

1. The almost *undefined anatomy* which is generally the object of the practice of operations research, compared with the well-defined *Homo sapiens* who is the object of the practice of the medical profession. Whether

---

[3] Talcott Parsons, "Some Problems Confronting Sociology as a Profession," *American Sociological Review*, vol. 24, no. 4 (August 1959), p. 547.

[4] Charles Singer, "History of Medicine," *Encyclopaedia Britannica* (Chicago: 1960), vol. 15, p. 199.

[5] Ibid., p. 201.

the patient is from the Sahara or Sibera, the medical doctor is given a clearly defined organism, while the operations researcher is not certain whether the object of his practice is a unicorn, an elephant, or a human being. If the animal under treatment itself is not defined, there can hardly be agreement on what part of the organism must be studied to identify the trouble.

2. Stemming from this undefined nature of the anatomy under treatment, operations research does not have available to it *normative measures* similar to those available to the medical practitioner. If the man from Siberia or the Sahara were to register a temperature of 103°F, it would be a clear signal of ailment to the medical practitioner. But in the case of operations research the anatomy is ill-defined; and how can there be normative measurements of an ill-defined anatomy? Does an inventory of 10 percent of current sales constitute a satisfactory condition, or does 20 percent, so that if inventory is say 25 percent or 15 percent, then the operations research practitioner can consider it as clear a signal as 103°F or 93°F is to the medical practitioner?

3. Scientific *diagnostic tools* available to the medical profession do not have any parallels in operations research. X-rays, electrocardiographs, blood counts, and the like aid the medical practitioner to test the correctness or incorrectness of his preliminary diagnosis with considerable degree of precision *prior* to actual implementation of prescriptions themselves. This makes the diagnostic effort in operations research more hazardous than in medicine. Modern information-processing equipment is helpful in making manageable the consideration of simultaneous interaction among several variables. However, a computer report is a far cry from an X-ray. While the latter is an exact picture of the organism, the most efficient electronic processing can at best represent different sketches relating to the organism, none of them as true as a photograph.

Thus, the present-day practice of operations research has some parallels to the state of the medical art around 500 B.C. characterized by "some skill in surgery and a very little knowledge of anatomy." Even when the knowledge of the anatomy is woefully inadequate, "surgery of sorts" is being performed out of desperation. Even as the devastation caused by the epidemics of the sixteenth century acted as the necessity which, in some sense, became the mother of the "invention" of modern medicine, so also the inventory losses sustained in the 1930's by American business may be looked upon as the necessity mediating the "invention" of industrial operations research, and the exigencies of World War II — the "invention" of military operations research.

The "surgery of sorts" born out of necessity can aid in understanding the anatomy on which such surgery is performed. In order to accomplish this understanding, the state of the organism before and after the surgery must be compared. Several pairs of "before" and "after" states of similar organisms can probably facilitate the understanding of why the observed responses of organisms came about as they did. And step-by-step "surgery of sorts" can shed light on different types of managerial decision-making organisms.

WHAT IS OPERATIONS RESEARCH?

We offer the following definition of operations research:

> Operations research is the heuristic art of prescriptive application of the scientific method to executive-type problems, whose solutions are not immediately obvious, and which arise in behavioral aspects of entities, more or less with respect to decision-making, in industrial, commercial, military and/or institutional environments.[6]

At this stage of development, operations research remains an art — a heuristic art. Its concern is with problem-solving, and with implementing the solution. George Polya describes his book *How to Solve It* (Princeton, 1945), as *heuristic*, a word which means "serving to discover." While Polya's excellent treatment in the book refers primarily to problems in geometry, what he seeks to systematize is the attempt at problem-solving in general. Operations research is concerned with problem-solving where executive-type decisions are involved, where conflicting demands on limited resources which have alternative uses need to be resolved at a managerial level.

At least equally as important as the solution to a specific resource allocation problem are the insights into the interrelationships among the various elements of the decision-affecting and decision-affected body.

An *in*efficient way to learn about the interrelationships germane to decision-making situations is to enumerate *all* possible combinations of elements entering into such situations. There are two basic defects to this approach. One is the utter astronomic proportions of the problem in even relatively simple situations. The other is the need for "distorted understanding."

---

[6] George K. Chacko, review article, *Operations Research* (September — October, 1961), p. 760.

On the first point, W. Ross Ashby[7] points out that a simple simulation involving all the details of men, weapons, and terrain of a large unit can, in principle, be loaded on a computer that is big enough. However, if the best tactic is to be discovered by investigating all the possible histories of engagements it would involve calculations of the order of 10^{500}.

The fastest computers available today perform 10^7–10^8 calculations[8] per minute. The forseeable future speeds would be in the range of 10^{11}–10^{12}. Thus 1,000,000 hours of the fastest forseeable computers can perform only calculations of the order of 10^{20}, a far cry from Ashby's estimate of 10^{500} required. Some reduction of the data is definitely in order. Complete enumeration, even if useful, is computationally infeasible.

Turning to the second point, the need for a "distorted understanding," we find an instructive parallel in the human body as it functions under the command and control of the brain.

> Let me borrow a page from Lord Adrian, the great British neurologist, to illustrate. If you set out to map that remarkable human organization, the human body, you make a chart of the anatomy, showing the bone structure, the heart, the lungs, etc. But the pattern of information within the body *about* the body is totally different. The various system projects the body into the brain, but it does not by any means project precisely the anatomical or physical structure into the brain. . . . If you consider the number of nerve endings in the various parts of the body, . . . the thumb is enormous and the fingers are large, but the arms are almost nonexistent. The lips are tremendous, the eyes are again enormous, but we have shortened legs, virtually no thighs and no behinds. In other words, our bodies look totally different: the organs of sense are magnified out of all proportion. This is the way the brain obtains information about the state of the body it controls, and this is the way it passes on orders to those parts of the body it can use. It is also noteworthy that the brain sometimes expresses preferences, by wanting to be informed in more detail about certain body phenomena at certain occasions. This is achieved by suppressing other — simultaneous — information or signals, in order to avoid confusion due to too many signals at one and the same time.[9]

In other words, irrespective of the availability of computer

---

[7] W. Ross Ashby, paper presented to Second Symposium in General Systems Theory, Case Institute of Technology, Cleveland, Ohio (April 1963).

[8] Private communication to the author.

[9] Oskar Morgenstern, "How to Plan to Beat Hell," *Fortune* (January 1963), p. 204.

facilities, the data have to be ordered beforehand, just as the brain chooses to study only a part of the vast array of information. The collection of data presupposes hypothesis about the interrelationships of the decision-affecting and decision-affected body.

If it is not even known for sure whether the object of operations research practice is an elephant or a bumblebee, or a whale or a human animal, and if much less is known about the decision-making of the respective organisms, then anything but the most discerning collection of data would turn out to be almost totally irrelevant to the solution of the problem.

The upshot of the foregoing is that operations research has a well-established domain no matter how fast computational capabilities become: the domain of diagnostics, perceiving "diseases" in "symptoms" even without definitely knowing much about the anatomy being treated; the domain of solutions, and of implementation of solutions. As definitive knowledge of the anatomies treated progresses, the method of problem-solving can be generalized; but at the present stage the practice of operations research remains an art, as distinguished from a science, in the sense that the latter predominantly deals with repeatable phenomena, and the former predominantly with nonrepeatable phenomena.

Yet the insights from the individual instances of artistic practice can be skillfully used to contribute to increasingly scientific generalizations of problem-solving. However, if emphasis is placed on symptomatic remedies, or techniques, it would be like trying to expound internal medicine on the basis of, say, "aspirin and the diseases it can cure," "penicillin and the diseases it can cure," "streptomycin and the diseases it can cure," etc. On the other hand, if emphasis is placed on diagnosis and prescription, these would relate to "diseases of ear-nose-throat region," "diseases of heart, lungs, and aorta," "diseases of stomach, pancreas, kidney," etc., and the process of perception of diseases practiced success-fully, as well as unsuccessfully, in different instances can be used to gain insights into the nature of the anatomy under treatment.

Instances of headache, stuffy nose, and upset stomach are shown in Figure 2. The "techniques" approach to managerial decision-making problems can be symbolized by treatment of these symptoms of ailment with ready-made remedies, like a particular brand of programming — Brand L — for headache, of inventory, and a particular brand of theory — Brand Q — for upset stomach of delayed shipments, etc.

The parallel between "techniques" and symptomatic relief they afford is illustrated in Figure 3. Aching head may be compared with high

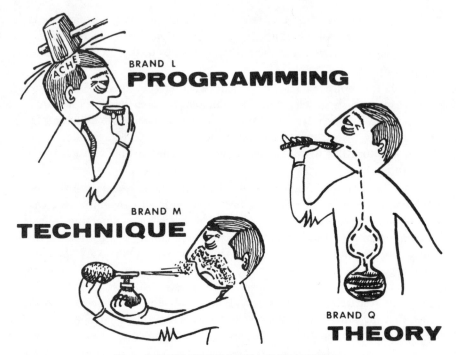

BRAND L
PROGRAMMING

BRAND M
TECHNIQUE

BRAND Q
THEORY

Figure 2. "TECHNIQUES" APPROACH TO AILMENTS.

inventory, upset stomach with delayed shipments, and runny nose with uncontrolled production process. These ailments are treated by ready-made remedies illustrated in Figure 4. Just as, say, Bufferin is applied to relieve headache, neuritis, neuralgia, etc., Brand L Programming is applied for inventory control, for production scheduling, for transportation problems. Similarly, Pepto-Bismol and the ailments it can alleviate can be paralleled with Brand Q Theory and all the disorders that it can cure. The points of departure of the present volume from the Technique books are broadly outlined in Figure 5; namely, the emphasis on concepts, instead of techniques; on diagnosis, instead of relief; and on the overall or organismic view, instead of sectional or atomistic view.

Operations research is applicable to industrial, commercial, military, and institutional environments. An industry refers to a group of firms which produce identical or closely similar products. Industrial environments are therefore predominantly oriented towards production processes. Commerce involves the exchange of products for a consideration, usually money. Basic to commercial activity is the exchange process, usually associated with marketing functions.

Figure 3. SYMPTOMATIC RELIEF.

Military environments are predominantly concerned with the question of national defense. The war for which preparations are made is not fought yet; hopefully it will never be. The efficacy of the national defense posture brought about through military preparedness hinges not so much on the production of military weapons and weapon systems as on the ability of the system to deter war. Most of these aspects of national defense refer to the future. The basic objective of the military system is the *D-factor*: *deterrence potential, destruction potential.*

Institutional activity comprises creative processes generally undertaken in the public interest. There is an element of public support associated with institutional activity, the intangible element being public opinion and the tangible element public contributions. The mandate to be creatively contributing to human understanding sometimes forces the institutions to outstrip public opinion, even at the expense of public support by way of contributions. If the objective of the military institutions' is the *physical* survival of the society, that of the institutional activity can be characterized as the survival of the society's *spiritual* self.

DRUGS	TECHNIQUES
BUFFERIN	***(BRAND L)*** **PROGRAMMING**
• Headache	• Inventory Control
• Arthritis	• Production Scheduling
• Neuralgia	• Transportation
• Neuritis	• Warehousing
PEPTO BISMOL	***(BRAND Q)*** **THEORY**
• • •	• • •

Figure 4. READY-MADE REMEDIES.

Points of Departure "TECHNIQUE" BOOKS	TODAY'S INFORMATION FOR TOMORROW'S PRODUCTS An Operations Research Approach
TECHNIQUES	CONCEPTS
RELIEF	DIAGNOSIS
SECTIONAL (Atomistic)	OVER-ALL (Organismic)

Figure 5. POINTS OF DEPARTURE.

OSMAL (ORGANIC SYMPTOMATIC MANIFESTATION LOCATION)

While it is the whole organism which is affected, or afflicted, the symptoms are located in one or more constituents of the organism, even as the disorder of the human body is manifested by symptoms in one or more parts of the body, e.g., ache in the head, a running nose, upset condition of the stomach. But considered properly as disorders of the organism-as-a-whole, the cause of the headache or of the runny nose is not exclusively sought in the locations of the manifestation of the symptom, namely, the head or the nose. The medical doctor is not generally instructed by the patient: "I have a headache; look into my head, and nowhere else." But the operations researcher has to be prepared for such an instruction: "We have an inventory problem; do some scheduling."

In operations research practice, it is essential that the *locations* where symtoms are manifested, e.g., accumulated inventory in the production department, are identified in conjunction with the *organismic symptoms*. Remedial measures are administered locally, even as in the case of the human body. Changes brought about in the decision-making in the production procedures, in the accounting system, in the allocation of research and development funds — are all instances of local administration of remedies not merely or even primarily for the betterment of the location, but for the betterment of the organism as a whole. We have to refer to these locations of manifestation of organismic symptoms, and these locations where remedial measures are administered, while keeping in mind their relationship to the whole.

Toward this end we shall refer to Organismic Symptomatic Manifestation Location (OSMAL). Thus, accounting is an OSMAL; standard costs is another OSMAL; so is preventive maintenance — as long as the location is the locale of manifestation of an organismic symptom, and as long as remedial measures can be meaningfully discussed and implemented with reference to the location.

SCIENTIFIC METHOD AND OPERATIONS RESEARCH

Aristotle refers to two constituents of the scientific method: (1) induction (2) explanation. Induction is the establishment of a universal truth by consideration of an instance or instances which reveal to thought the necessity of the connection asserted. Explanation may be understood as the knowledge of causes of phenomena.

These two pronouncements of Aristotle determined the course of the discussion about scientific method for more than two thousand years. Thus Francis Bacon, David Hume, and J. S. Mill all assumed that the business of the empirical scientist was to establish universal propositions about causal connection, though they differed from Aristotle in the accounts they gave of causes. Francis Bacon, for instance, held that the business of the scientist is to discover the forms of phenomena, but in his usage this word "form" means what would now be called a necessary and sufficient condition. However, when Bacon wrote his *Novum Organum* at the beginning of the seventeenth century, the policy of making hypotheses for the purpose of primary and secondary induction was a novelty and not very well understood. The modern definitions of primary and secondary inductions are as follows:

> Primary induction is the deliberate attempt to find more laws about the behavior of the things that we can observe and so to draw the bounds of natural possibility more narrowly . . . . Secondary induction is the attempt to incorporate the results of primary induction in any explanatory theory covering a large field of inquiry.[10]

It is of the essence of induction to set up principles from which we can derive observable facts and applications of observed facts. On what grounds do we accept some statements of principles and not others? We can distinguish between two reasons for accepting a principle:

> One reason for believing a statement is that we can derive results from it which can be checked by observation; in other words, we believe in a statement because of its consequences. For example, we believe in Newton's laws because we can calculate from them the motions of the celestial bodies. The second reason for belief — is that we can believe a statement because it can be derived logically from intelligible principles.[11]

No hypothesis can be "proved" by experiment. Experiment only "confirms" a hypothesis. When confirmed, it leads to the support of a theory which is simpler than a mere record of observations, and which can predict the expected range of observations. If we require complete agreement, we can certainly achieve it by merely recording the observations. However, nobody would regard this record as acceptable theory, although it is in complete agreement with our observations.

> What makes a theory is the quality of being simpler and shorter than the record of observations. Hence, the acceptance of a theory is always the result of a compromise between the requirement of "agreement with the facts," and of "simplicity."[12]

---

[10] W. C. Knele, "Scientific Method," *Encyclopaedia Britannica* (Chicago: 1960), vol. 20, p. 129.

[11] Philipp Frank, *Philosophy of Science: The Link Between Science and Philosophy* (Englewood Cliffs, N. J.: Prentice-Hall, Inc., 1957), p. 16.

[12] Philipp Frank, *Philosophy of Science, op. cit.*, p. 353.

The scientific method is based on: (1) an abiding faith in the rationality of nature, (2) the idea of statistical control, and (3) experimentalism as the method of gathering evidence.

The abiding faith in the rationality of nature is the faith that phenomena have causes. The line between observation and explanation itself has to be constructed by means of a theory. However, in order that such a connection should be attempted at all, there must be the basic faith that phenomena have arisen out of causes. By causes we mean the nexus of relationships which can be used to determine within limits, the juxtaposition of an entity with reference to successive reference points in the time-space continuum.

These causes must be repeatable; so also must be the results of these causes. If they do not repeat, then it will not be possible to construct a theory to chart the course of successive reference points of the· entity in the time-space conntinuum. Once this is possible, the effort is not so much to reproduce the identical reference points of the entity in the future as to reproduce within limits, within specifiable limits, within statistical limits, the recurrence of the predicted reference points of the entity. It is this repeatability which underlies many of the modern processes of manufacture and of measurement.

LIMITATION OF THE SCIENTIFIC METHOD IN OPERATIONS RESEARCH

Organismic phenomena of the type considered by operations research are not "dissectible," which imposes limitations on the application of the scientific method.

> Between the living world and the physical world, moreover, there is a critical distinction as regards dissectability. A watch spring can be taken out of a watch and its properties usefully studied apart from its normal setting. But if a heart be taken out of a live animal, then there is great limitation on the range of useful studies that can be made.[13]

The application of scientific method to operations research is thus greatly limited: (1) by the fact that the "heart" cannot be "taken out of" the living organism and studied usefully. (2) Furthermore, it is not even known for sure what the heart of the matter is, much less what the organism germane to the study itself is. Without knowing for sure the anatomy of the organism under study itself, we are hard put to assign objectives which are meaningful to the organism.

---

[13] Warren Weaver, "A Quarter Century in the Natural Sciences," *The Rockefeller Foundation Annual Report* (New York: 1958), p. 9.

The third limitation of the scientific method on operations research highlights the difference between the operations research studies and physiological studies. Christian Bohr observed that the specific task of physiology

> is to investigate the phenomena peculiar to the organism as a given empirical object in order to obtain an understanding of the various parts in the self-regulation and how they are balanced against each other and brought into harmony with variations in external influences and inner processes. It is thus in the very nature of this task to refer the word purpose to the maintenance of the organism and consider as purposive the regulation mechanisms which serve this maintenance.[14]

Thus, the "purpose" of the organism is a basic datum to the physiologist; the purpose of the organism is *not* a basic datum to the operations researcher: it has to be discovered, imputed, and successfully respecified by the operations researcher as continuing process.

In so imputing the purposiveness to the organism under study, the operations researcher seeks to extend insights from experience elsewhere, however imperfect, to the new situations under study. When there is no knowledge whatsoever of the organismic situation to be generated out of operations research studies, e.g., the first efforts at national development of a newly independent country, the "purpose" of such studies is far from known. Should the Gross National Product of the country be sought to be increased by 5 percent per year for the next five years? Or should the rate of capital formation be increased at twice the rate of growth of population? Any number of alternative combinations of specifiable objectives are available, but not one of them is a given purpose. The appearance of a charismatic leader in one country may conceivably accomplish marvels which are inconceivable in the absence of such leadership. Once a beaten path is made in the wilderness of "purpose," this purpose may be compared with the results obtained, and used to gauge the appropriateness of the path chosen to accomplish the purpose, as well as the appropriateness of the purposes themselves.*

The fourth limitation of the scientific method in operations

---

[14] Christian Bohr, "On Pathological Lung Expansion," *Anniversary Publication,* Copenhagen University, 1910, quoted in Niels Bohr, *Atomic Physics and Human Knowledge* (New York: John Wiley & Sons, Inc., 1958), p. 96.

*Basic measurements germane to national objectives of economic development via international coalitions, as well as their interrelationships, are derived from the largest set of continuous and comparable post-war data for 29 selected countries — NATO countries, Warsaw Pact countries, U.S. Allies, Unaligned countries — in the author's forthcoming volume: *National Self-Interest Measures: Sectoral Coefficients.*

research as compared with the scientific method in natural sciences is with respect to the ontological frame of reference. The ontological point of view, i.e., "referring to the subject matter of scientific knowledge which is independent of its relation to the perceiver," is the frame of reference for the natural sciences; but the subject matter of operations research knowledge is sometimes defined in the process of measuring it. As such, one could not readily speak about the subject matter "which is independent of its relation to the perceiver." In fact, the perceptiveness of the operations researcher is of the essence in transforming and solving the problem on hand.

EMPHASIS OF FLEXIBILITY IN ORGANISMIC RESEARCH

These limitations of the scientific method in operations research serve to highlight the need for flexibility to permit adaptive learning. As a first statement of the problem, we may recognize controllable and noncontrollable variables and specify action to be taken to influence the controllable variables. A third variable describes the effect of the action taken, designated as effect variable. Thus, three types may be identified: controllable, uncontrollable, and effect variables.

This statement — fairly standard — presupposes that distinction can be made among the three different kinds of variables. However, in the light of our discussion on pages 24-25, it is apparent that the very division into these three types is made with reference to *each* problem and *each* organism, by the operations researcher. Admittedly, there may be deduced certain invariance among the three types of variables. But from the conceptual point of view of operations research, such division is contingent upon the permissible guesses found applicable to the structure of the anatomy under study.

In a standard statement of the "inventory problem," the controllable variables may be the number of units of a particular product. The noncontrollable variable will be the consumer demand for the product. The effect variable will be the change in the cost of maintaining the inventory of the particular product in such a way that the probability of meeting the consumer demand is equal to a preassigned value.

In this instance we have assumed that the meeting of the consumer demand is the purpose of the organism. We have also assumed that the satisfaction of the demand for the particular product, in a particular manner, is an acceptable means to achieve this objective. However, the very fact that the demand is met in a particular way may have some effect on the demand itself. Thus, for instance, the supply of a particular good in lots less than 100 within twenty-four hours of receipt of the order may encourage the customers to order more frequently in smaller quantities. On the other hand, if particular savings are offered to the customer for purchase of quantities between say, 501 and 1,000, savings made possible because of inventory control, then there may be a perceptible change in the demand function.

The moral of this is that there is bound to be interaction between the demand for a product and the supply of it; and the particular means of supply and the structure of demand itself. Therefore the inventory policy has to be based on the treatment of variables which will be controllable at one point in time, and capable of changing from noncontrollable to controllable at other points in time. It must be pointed out that the current approach in terms of "static analyses, stationary-state analyses, and dynamic analyses" of inventory problems does not build into it the change of status of variables from uncontrollable to controllable.

This volume develops certain concepts in operations research, and indicates their applications to business and military situations. How the problem has been viewed is more important than what has been accomplished in the particular instance. Different organisms are studied in the different problems, and insights derived from apparently dissimilar situations are built into connected elements of an approach to understanding, analyzing, solving, and implementing solutions to managerial decision-making problems.

. . . The wise man looks into space, and does not regard the small as too little, nor the great as too big; for he knows that there is no limit to dimensions.

LAO-TSE

CHAPTER TWO

ORDERING OF OBJECTIVES

The proverbial sixsome who went to "see" the elephant were blind. Their main means of data collection was the sense of touch. Although the sense of touch reported rather faithfully the findings of each of the investigators, difficulties arose when projections were made on the basis of individual observations of sample size one. The projections varied with the individual investigator, and were limited by previous experience.

None of the blind men had ever really "seen" an elephant. They did not know what it was or what it was like. In this respect, they were like the wise man who "looks into space" to fathom the mystery and meaning of life. When he peers into the unknown, he ought to have some idea about what he is looking for, so that he could recognize the object of his search if he saw it. Similarly, the blind men hypothesized that there was some thing or being called an elephant, and literally tried to put their fingers on just what it was.

Each blind man claimed that his particular investigation told him *all* about the object of inquiry. The moving trunk suggested a snake to one blind man; the moving ear indicated a fan to another; the stationary torso, a wall; the stationary leg, a pillar, and so on. While correct in their respective characterizations, the individual investigations erred in attributing wholeness to the part.

The reason that the parts were each claimed to be the whole lies in the *unit of measurement* each investigator adopted. All of them were trying to specify the entity, called the unknown, the "X," or the "elephant." For this, they collected data. Data collection requires specific units in which to report the findings. These units may be ordinal, or cardinal. The ordinal units permit statements of the type: "A is equal to, greater than, or less than B"; while the cardinal units are read off a scale with a zero point, and a measure specifying the distance between 0 and 1 on the scale.

Admittedly, the unit of measurement chosen should be appropriate to whatever is being specified: an attribute, a characteristic, a relationship. The unit of meaurement chosen to "see" the elephant is seldom the same as that employed in understanding "the mystery and meaning of life."

By the same token, the unit of measurement chosen by the investigator reflects the investigator's view of whatever is being specified. "Beauty is in the eye of the beholder" because he is looking for beauty in ordinal units; and his view is not necessarily shared by anyone else unless "beauty" is represented by cardinal units — and specifications are made in terms of these cardinal units, or the ordinal units are somehow shared in common.

The blind men used ordinal units, not cardinal. Therefore they could establish meaningful communication with each other without either translating the ordinals into cardinals or making the ordinals comparable one with the other simply by sharing the ordinal measures.

When employing ordinal units, no less when employing cardinal units, *flexibility* is essential. The flexibility is with reference both to the measures and to what they represent. Thus when the blind investigator of the elephant's trunk declared that the elephant was capable of moving like a snake, he should have been prepared to admit another investigator's declaration that the object of their specification could also be stationary like a wall. There was no meeting of the minds because the possibility was not admitted that the same object could be both stationary and in motion at the same time.

The flexibility in processing data in order to understand the source of data is governed by the *interrelationships* of data generated. If the data gathered are acceptable, the data from different sources should be *jointly interpreted*. Thus, to reconcile two types of movement like a snake and a fan *simultaneously* with two types of stationary status like a wall and a pillar, the investigators would have to visualize some interrelationships permitting sectional movement.

Thus the collection of data requires units of measurement; the selection of units of measurement reflects the investigator's view of whatever is being specified. When employing either ordinal or cardinal units to understand phenomena, interrelationships of data have to be recognized so that the views of the organism under investigation held hitherto would be accepted or rejected meaningfully from the overall point of view of the search.

It is inevitable in such a process that some evidences which ought to be discarded will be accepted, and some which ought to be accepted will be discarded. One safeguard against indiscriminate acceptance or rejection of evidence is the hypothesized interrelationship of the *seen* components as part of the *unseen* whole. Charting the pilgrimage of inquiry within this context suggests guidelines for ordering of objectives of the organism, which we examine next.

ORGANISMIC OBJECTIVES

There exists a long-term system of objectives for each organismic entity. The objectives may be prescribed by design, or arrived at by default. The long-term view of what-can-be with respect to the organism is a cornerstone of the organismic objectives system.

What are some of the guidelines in arriving at the objectives of any given organism? The guidelines should be general enough to be applicable over industrial, commercial, military and institutional environments; but should be specific enough to be meaningful to the particular problem on hand.

One of the prime objectives of any organism is self-preservation. However, the operations researcher has to skilfully choose (1) which organism is to achieve self-preservation, and (2) what state of the organism is to be preserved. He may have to put the corporation ahead of its divisions; he may have to put the defense of the whole country ahead of the primacy of a particular Service. He may have to choose long-term growth over immediate gains; he may have to choose strategic defense capabilities over tactical defense capabilities.

Organismic objectives must be stated in measurable terms. Without quantification, the consequences of actions taken to influence the course of events cannot be compared with the original goals in a clear-cut fashion. Without a consistent scheme of comparison of goals with accomplishments, there cannot be instituted a progressive translation of what-ought-to-be into what-is.

It is essential that intended changes to be brought about by proposed actions be specified in terms of *units of measurement.* Thus, an "inventory problem" could be claimed to have been "solved" by cutting down production, or substituting custom-job-type operation for large-scale manufacture. If the unit of measurement is "inventory pieces" or "inventory cost," the claim would seem to have been sustained. However, if "net profit at full capacity operation" were the unit of measurement, such a unit would suggest that simultaneous with the gain in reducing inventory, losses in production efficiency, rise in unit production cost of items, unrealizable large-size sales, unrealizable advantage in reputation for ready shipment, etc., should be taken into account.

The need for organismic units of measurement, capable of reflecting the consequences to the organism as a whole and not merely to the parts where changes are introduced, is underscored by the fact that *any* change would leave the organism a different entity than before the introduction of the change. Without previously agreed upon units of measurement, support can be found for practically any position about the consequences of the changes introduced, merely by selecting convenient data, conveniently measured in convenient units. Previous selection pinpoints the claims and enables evaluation. Also, prior agreement tends to ensure that the units of measures do reflect organismic activity as a whole, and not merely that of the part(s) to be influenced by the activity. Removal of the headache can indeed be unsatisfactory if it is only traded for a stomachache.

STRATEGIC OBJECTIVES

Strategic Objectives: Profit-Making Environments

Organismic objectives are long-term goals. They refer to the organism as a whole. What are the consequences of the organismic objectives in the short run, and for the constituent parts of the organism?

Starting with the broad dichotomy between industrial and commercial environments on the one hand, and military and institutional environments on the other, of profit-making vs. nonprofit-making, we may inquire into the mechanics of accomplishing the long-term goal.

In order to accomplish the objective of profits in the long run, it will be helpful to have profits in the short run, and to have them consistently. However, with changing consumer demand in order to maintain profits in the long run, new ways to satisfy the changing demand are called for. This means investments in research and development, prototype and promotion: which are time-taking activities. Once they become successful, the investments made will be paid back in profits. These new avenues of return on investment can accelerate the rate of profit and the volume of profits accruing to the organism. However, the earning of profits needs not necessarily be a uniform and continuous phenomenon.

In terms of the organismic objectives of profit-making in the long run, it is quite feasible to break even or even sustain losses in the short run in some of the constituent parts of the corporation. Interim nonrealization of the organismic objectives is consistent, within limits, with the long-term realization of the organismic objective.

Strategic Objectives: Nonprofit-Making Environments

Turning to the military environment, we find that the objective of survival cannot be left unrealized at any time. However, there is a complicated problem of evaluating exactly when this does or does not happen. If the deterrent potential or the destruction potential were found wanting, then the military environment would have failed in its objective of survival.

The deterrent potential depends on the credibility to the prospective enemy, of the destruction potential and the will to use the destruction potential. More important than the actual destruction capability is what the prospective enemy *believes* to be the destruction capability; and more important than the actual will to use the destruction potential is what the enemy *believes* to be the will to pull the trigger.*

The role of strategic objectives assumes fresh significance in military environments even when the evaluation of organismic objectives continues to be rather nebulous. To the members of the Defense organism, national survival in the event of a global war and the prevention of such a global war are too broad an objective. Recalling Lord Adrian's "need for distorted understanding" of the different parts of the body by the brain (see

---

*The implications for policy of the "bluffs" relating to capability as converted into "threats" of credibility are examined elsewhere in the author's forthcoming volume: *Strategies of Survival in Nonconfrontary Encounter.*

page 16), the constituent members of the Defense organism will necessarily function in response to the dictates of the local command system which would elevate to imperative dimensions, say, the preventive maintenance in the motor pool. The measurement of effectiveness of overall military preparedness at any time would, by its sheer size, impel the pursuit of strategic objectives in the short run by the different components of the Defense organism which may be at variance with the organismic objective or somewhat unrelated to it.

TACTICAL OBJECTIVES

The immediate, instead of the near future, is often the arena in which the organism seeks to survive. The issues range from the acceptance of a production lot to the quotation of price on a single order. These are neither the wars nor the battles, but only skirmishes. But skirmishes do influence the outcome of battles and of wars. The loss of a nail on the horseshoe in this context may lead to the loss of an entire kingdom.

Tactical objectives are generally determined very much by the conditions in the field. The field forces are perilously far away from the top management which is familiar with the organismic objectives, and the middle management which is familiar with the strategic objectives. Therefore the scope of activity by the field force must be very carefully delimited beforehand. As far as the field forces are concerned, the successful writing of a particular sales order is of utmost importance. To this end, lower price quotations may be offered as an immediate tactic. Consequences of this move can be far-reaching. For instance, the price reduction for a particular product in a particular order can bind the company to bring down prices to the same level in all its transactions with all the other dealings with customers. Thus, the immediate winning of the skirmish of the single order, representing say $1,000, may in fact be directly responsible for a loss as high as, say, $100,000 across the board. Nor is the damage confined to the particular product for which the lower quotation is made. In line with the reduction made in the *single* transaction, the customers of other products probably demand an appropriate downward adjustment in prices.

Even as the speed of an army is that of the slowest soldier, the accomplishment of organismic objectives would depend very heavily on the performance of each of the moves circumscribed by the tactical objectives, developed somewhat on an ad hoc basis on the spot. At least some of the individual skirmishes need to be won; but the choice of circumstances should not be left to the field forces lest, in winning battles, they lose the war outlined by strategic objectives and organismic objectives.

OBJECTIVES: UNITED STATES TRAVEL SERVICE

What are the organismic objectives, strategic objectives and tactical objectives of United States Travel Service? In turn, what objectives — organismic, strategic and tactical — should guide the profit-making Advertising Agencies which bid for the account of United States Travel Service?

The Department of Commerce appointed four advertising agencies in August 1961 to do the initial research and planning for the newly established Travel Service. An outlay of $3,500,000 for a "Sell America" advertising and promotion campaign overseas was planned. This outlay was to be the initial size of the account to be handled by one or more advertising agencies.

For the client, the United States Travel Service, if the organismic objective is stated as an increase in the flow of foreign tourists into the United States, then in order to measure the results of the advertising campaign effectively, the flow of foreign tourists in the absence of such campaign should be predetermined.

In formulating the organismic objectives of the United States Travel Service, attention should be given to the nonprofit-making nature of the venture. Stimulation to the United States economy as a result of tourist spending then becomes a secondary and a side effect. The organismic objective itself can be stated as increase in international understanding. By this standard, the mere number of additional toursits who visit the United States would not accomplish the objective. The strategic objectives would include choice of a symbol of identification. If the organismic objectives were merely the additional number of foreign tourists, the emphasis could very well be upon the sights and scenery. If, on the other hand, emphasis is placed on the improvement of international understanding, the symbol has to be indicative of the intangibles which make America the nation it is. If Las Vegas were to symbolize the former, the Statue of Liberty would symbolize the latter. In fact, the French Tourist Office account, now handled by Doyle Dane Bernbach, Inc., treats subject matter ranging from Norman inns to Nice bathing beauties.

Without clear formulation of organismic objectives and strategic objectives, it is not difficult to see how *tactical objectives*, left to the devisings of the far-flung field force, can defeat the former. At the tactical objective level, we may visualize a single foreign tourist being cajoled, coaxed, and perhaps lured into visiting the United States — only to discover to his dismay that the economy trip had far outrun his means almost before he got started. This concentration on the part of the field force on the mere number of foreign tourists could conceivably lead to success of the tactical objective at the cost of strategic and organismic objectives. If improved international understanding is at all a significant objective of the organism, the flow of traffic should be qualitatively restricted. Indiscriminate encouragement of tourist traffic can very well ruin the purposes which may have stimulated the encouragement of foreign tourist trade in the first place.

OBJECTIVES: PARTICIPATING U.S. ADVERTISING AGENCIES

While the organismic objective of the United States Travel Service is nonprofit-making, that of the advertising agencies participating in the campaign is profit-making. Within the profit-making orientation, what types of objectives may be reasonably attributed to the organisms of the four agencies appointed by the Department of Commerce to do the initial research and planning for the United States Travel Office?

One of the four agencies is Interpublic, Inc. Walter Johnson, a general corporate executive who is the senior adviser on travel accounts for Interpublic, says: "Within a decade, the travel industry will be the biggest business in the world."[1] If this statement is any guide, the organismic objective of Interpublic, may be concerned not merely with the new United States tourist effort but with the travel industry as a whole.

If capturing a share of the worldwide tourist trade promotion via promoting the United States Travel Service is the organismic objective of Interpublic, then the means to accomplish this end in the near future and in the immediate future would be selected accordingly. Consider promotional literature that the Agency can use in behalf of its client; and consider also the persuasive role in choosing locations for foreign offices of the United States Travel Service. If worldwide travel industry promotion is the concern of the organismic objective, then the success in the latter may be more important than the success in the former. In fact, it may be worthwhile for the Agency to give up selling to the United States Travel Service a few pieces of promotional literature in order to redirect the Agency staff to persuading the client on the choice of an office site, which in turn becomes a new built-in source of demand for promotion.

The allocation of the time and effort of the Agency will be directed according to the stakes associated with the success or failure of promotional literature, site selection, etc. In arriving at the stakes themselves, the Agency will have to do its own computation of the possible importance attached to each of these by the client, the United States Travel Service. If

---

[1] Walter Johnson, "U.S. Travel Service," *New York Times* (Aug. 13, 1961), p. 12F.

the organismic objective of the client is merely to increase the number of foreign tourists in the United States, mass appeal which will reach the maximum potential of tourists would be accorded high importance. On the other hand, if the organismic objective of the Travel Service is to increase international understanding via tourist traffic, emphasis would be on selective, instead of mass, appeal.

ALTERNATIVE OBJECTIVES STRATEGIES

Having identified the major types of strategies, we inquire: (1) how can we represent the different types of strategies so that they are logically consistent? (2) how can we *compare* the alternative strategies available at any one time so that selection may be made from among them? and (3) how can we differentiate between hierarchies of objectives within the same family of objectives when they are pursued at different levels?

A Strategy is a group of organismic, strategic, and tactical objectives pertaining to the same situation. Thus, if the United States Travel Service organismic objective is to increase the number of tourists into the United States, the U.S. advertising companies bidding for the account can choose the strategic objective of providing a symbol of identification, and the tactical objective of making promotional pieces. Thus,

STRATEGY A:
(Organismic) Increase the Number of Tourists into the U.S.
(Strategic) Provide a Symbol of Identification
(Tactical) Make Promotional Pieces

Consistent with the organismic objective of increasing the number of tourists is another strategic objective, viz., increasing the number of field offices of the United States Travel Service (U.S.T.S.). The Advertising Agencies would then want to aid and assist the client, U.S.T.S., to locate the field offices.

STRATEGY B:
(Organismic) Increase the Number of Tourists into the U.S.
(Strategic) Increase the Number of Field Offices of U.S.T.S.
(Tactical) Aid in location studies for Field Offices

Here we have two different strategies. According to the first one, the tactical objective of the Agency should be to make promotional pieces; according to the second one, the tactical objective of the Agency should be to aid in location studies for the Field Offices of the client. How can we represent the two strategies so that logical consistency may be established?

To put it differently, how can we represent the hierarchy of strategies so that the odd constituents would stand out? Thus,

(Strategic) Provide a Symbol of Identification
(Tactical) Aid in location studies for the Field Offices does *not* suggest a logical hierarchy of objectives; neither does

(Strategic) Increase the Number of Field Offices of U.S.T.S.
(Tactical) Make Promotional Pieces

Therefore, we need to devise a numbering system which suggests automatically that the components are ill-matched.

Let us designate the organismic objective of increasing the number of tourists into the United States by the number 1. In order to show that the strategic objectives are of a lower order than the organismic, and at the same time, that the strategic objectives are a part of the 1 group, we may assign the number 1.1 or 11 to the strategic objective corresponding to 1. The tactical objective corresponding to 1 and 11 can be designated 1.1.1 or 111. Thus,

STRATEGY A: organismic objective (1)
strategic objective (11)
tactical objective (111)

If the strategic objective of providing a symbol of identification is designated 11, the strategic objective of increasing the number of field offices of U.S.T.S. can be designated 12. Similarly, if the tactical objective of making promotional pieces is designated 111, the tactical objective of aiding in location studies for the Field Offices can be designated 121. Thus,

STRATEGY B: organismic objective (1)
strategic objective (12)
tactical objective (121)

We notice that Strategy A and Strategy B both have the same organismic objective of increasing the number of tourists into the U.S. It is desirable to differentiate between the two Strategy A's. If the identity of the organismic objective needs to be emphasized, a two-digit numbering system can be used: Strategy 10, Strategy 11.

But, even as (1, 11, 111) and (1, 12, 121) branch off from the same organismic objective, 1, so also there can be a class of organismic objectives of which 1 is a particular choice. Thus, U.S.T.S. can have as organismic objective, improving international understanding, designated as, say, 2, or improving the quality of tourists into the United States, designated as, say, 3.

It behooves the advertising agency to differentiate between hierarchies of objectives. Thus, improving international understanding can be achieved through improving the quality of tourists into the United States, which in turn can be attempted through increased number of tourists into the U.S. These three are all organismic objectives, and may be distinguished from one another by assigning them to a consistent scheme of "grades" of objectives.

The most comprehensive organismic objective, and the most general, may be assigned "grade 1." In this instance, improving international understanding may be assigned "grade 1." The most operative statement of organismic objective, and the most specific in operational or near-operational terms, may be assigned "grade 3"; e.g., increase the number of tourists into the U.S.

By associating each "grade" with a "level," the number of possible distinctions can be multiplied; e.g., three grades and three levels permit nine combinations.

The U.S.T.S. organismic objective of improving international understanding can be considered "Grade 1: level 3." The higher levels, "2" and "1" can be represented by 0.3 or 03 (Grade 1: level 2), and 0.003 or 003 (Grade 1: level 1).

In Table I the alternative objectives strategies are assigned numbers in a consistent manner. The advertising agency can identify its own position on the spectrum of possible objectives of U.S.T.S. Associated with each Strategy it chooses to employ, a consistent scheme of (organismic, strategic, tactical) objectives is worked out; and each Strategy can be compared with other possible Strategies. Some of the Strategies are not feasible under the capabilities of the organism; and some Strategies suggest higher payoffs than others. The choice will have to be made between the possible Strategies open to the organism, and the types of risks the organism is willing to undertake. The ranking of the objectives and the number scheme shown are purely for illustrative purposes.

TABLE I

ALTERNATIVE OBJECTIVES STRATEGIES

Objectives	GRADE 1	GRADE 2	GRADE 3	
Organismic				
Level 1	003*	002†	001‡	001
Level 2	03	02	01	01
Level 3	3	2	1	1
Strategic				
Level 1				
Level 2				
Level 3			11	12
Tactical				
Level 1				
Level 2				
Level 3			111	121

Strategy 10 : (1, 11, 111)
Strategy 11 : (1, 12, 121)

*Improve international understanding.
†Improve the quality of tourists in the U.S.
‡Increase the number of tourists into the U.S.

OBJECTIVES: UNITED STATES DEFENSE

The consistency of ranking of objectives may be considered further with respect to the United States Defense organismic objectives on the one hand, and, on the other, the corresponding guide to the defense contractors who bid for contracts for equipment and systems.

> We must be able to make deliberate choice in weapons and strategy, shift the tempo of our production and alter the direction of our forces to meet rapidly changing conditions or objectives at very short notice and under any circumstances. Our weapons system must be usable in a manner permitting deliberation and discrimination as to timing, scope, and targets in response to civilian authority; and our defenses must be secure against prolonged reattack as well as surprise first strike. To purchase productive capacity and to initiate development programs that may never need to be used — as this budget proposes — adopts an insurance policy of buying alternative future options.[2]

Considering the organismic objectives of the United States, four

[2] John F. Kennedy, Special Defense-Budget Message to the Congress, March 28, 1961.

major areas may be delineated, which are discernible in President Kennedy's Budget Message.

I. ALTERNATIVE ACTION OBJECTIVES   (A Area)

II. BALANCED BUDGET OBJECTIVE   (B Area)

III. COMMAND AND CONTROL OBJECTIVES (C Area)

IV. DETERRENCE AND DESTRUCTION
     OBJECTIVES   (D Area)

If these are the four overriding organismic objectives of the United States, contractors bidding to supply equipment and systems for U.S. defense would be well advised to relate the *specific* contributions they intend to offer, to the *general* structure of organismic objectives.

Parallel to the "grades" illustrated in Table I, we can employ "Areas" to evolve a ranking system for U.S. Defense Objectives. We ranked the grades according to the comprehensive nature of the organismic objectives, the most comprehensive being "grade 1."

The four organismic objectives of U.S. Defense may also be ranked in order of importance. Since all the four objectives are comprehensive, we can try to assess their relative significance to U.S. Defense. It may be argued that the objective of balancing the budget can be sacrificed to attain the objective of deterrence and destruction, and the deterrence and destruction objective may be made second to the command and control objective which, in turn, may be superseded by the alternative action objective. Thus, Alternative Action Objectives (A Area) are assigned "grade 1," Command and Control Objectives (C Area), "grade 2," Deterrence and Destruction Objectives (D Area), "grade 3," and Balanced Budget Objectives (B Area), "grade 4."

In Table I we assigned to organismic objective "grade 3: level 3" the number 1, and to the corresponding strategic objective, the number 11, and to the corresponding tactical objective, the number 111. In other words, we moved by one additional place throughout the Table, whether it be organismic and strategic, or strategic and tactical; and whether it be grade 1 and grade 2, or grade 2 and grade 3.

In Table II we illustrate a different numbering system. Organismic objective "grade 1: level 3" is assigned the number 2,560,000. The corresponding strategic objective is 1,600, or the square root of 2,560,000. The corresponding tactical objective is the square root of 1,600, or 40.

TABLE II

ORDERING OF U. S. DEFENSE OBJECTIVES AND
CONSTITUENT ELEMENTS

Area Objectives	Alternative Action Objectives Area (A Area)	Command and Control Objectives Area (C Area)	Deterrence and Destruction Objectives Area (D Area)	Balanced Budget Objectives Area (B Area)
Organismic				
Level 1	7,680,000	2,430,000	480,000	300,000
Level 2	5,120,000	1,620,000	320,000	200,000
Level 3	2,560,000	810,000	160,000	100,000
Strategic				
Level 1	4,800	2,700	1,200	300
Level 2	3,200	1,800	800	200
Level 3	1,600	900	400	100
Tactical				
Level 1	120	90	60	30
Level 2	80	60	40	20
Level 3	40	30	20	10

Every entry in "level 2" is *twice* that of "level 3," and every entry in "level 1" is *thrice* that of "level 3."

OBJECTIVES: BIDDING U.S. DEFENSE CONTRACTORS

While the organismic objective of United States Defense is non-profit-making, that of the defense contractors who bid for the Defense contracts for equipment as well as systems is generally profit-making. Within the profit-making orientation, what guidelines for contract proposals may be established on the basis of the U.S. Defense organismic objectives?

The prime consideration is that the equipment, system or activity that the contractor is planning to offer in his bid for a Defense contract must be related to the hierarchy of the customer's objectives, illustrated in Table II. It is likely that more than one of the four organismic objectives cited earlier would be the object of the bid — in which case the contractor's evaluation of his own claim on the bid would depend on a composite score of the satisfaction anticipated to be provided by the subject of the bid.

If, for instance, alternative action objective of the customer is the aim of the subject of the bid, the bidding contractor may consider his best strength to lie in the flexibility of action that can be brought about by the subject of the bid. Thus if fighting both on land and in water is considered the organismic objective, then an armored tank which could travel on land as well as in water would provide the required flexibility.

However, the cost of developing such a vehicle may turn out to be extremely high, and may exceed the maximum share the vehicle can claim in the prosecution of the fighting. Here we have run up against the constraint imposed by another of the four major organismic objective, the B factor: budget allocations arrived at on the basis of overall requirements and resources may not permit the expenditures needed to develop such a vehicle.

But if the contractor were to assume that flexibility in fulfilling A area is supreme, and invests heavily in developing an amphibious tank, he may find himself having worked out of a contract because of the B area.

Where should the contractor draw the line? How would he know whether or not developing the amphibious tank would lead him to expend resources far beyond what the customer would be willing to invest? On the other hand, would not the risk-taking, in the form of building the amphibious tank pay off in the future when the customer suddenly recognized that in fact a much higher outlay than originally intended would be quite in order?

Perhaps. But he has no way of knowing for sure ahead of time. Yet, he has to make the decision today, *now*.

He can satisfy himself that the activity he has embarked upon is the best he can offer under the given circumstances. He can satisfy himself that the activity is consistent with what he considers to be the organismic objectives of the customer. He may want to be ready to shift gears and tempo at short notice. He has to be objectives-oriented, not equipment-bound. He has to be flexible in the deployment of his productive capacities, not rigid in their allocation. He has to take chances ingeniously, not rashly. Risk-taking is a necessary condition for profit-making, but not a sufficient condition. But he can increase the probability of realizing profit by ensuring that the chances he takes are intelligent.

Errors are inevitable in judgments about the future made in the present. There can be no complete guarantee against errors — except if one were to make no judgments on the future whatsoever. The probability of making errors has to be countered by the probability of making the right decisions at the right time. Every decision to bring about changes is circumscribed by technological constraints. Technological history discloses the limits within which innovations have taken place in the past and therefore the current limits on potential developments. These limits can guide the chartering of the efforts for future systems and equipment.

PART II

PROFILE OF POTENTIAL

Look: the constant marigold
Springs again from hidden roots.
Baffled gardener, you behold
New beginnings and new shoots.

ROBERT GRAVES, *"Marigolds"*

O! for a Muse of fire, that would ascend
The brightest heaven of invention!

WILLIAM SHAKESPEARE, *King Henry V, Prologue*

CHAPTER THREE

TECHNOLOGICAL FEASIBILITY
BASIS OF RESEARCH PLANNING

New beginnings and new shoots are bids against decay by the organism. New shoots appear in nature to take the place of the old, and if the new are more numerous than the old, the result is a net increase of the species. In nature, the replacement is generally closely akin to the replaced. But new beginnings in the man-made world are seldom similar to the entities they are replacing. While structurally seldom similar, the replacements remain *functionally compatible,* if accelerated and altered by technology.

The marigold is described as "constant." But the gardener is baffled because new shoots appear from almost nowhere. The roots are hidden; therefore the process of slow but sure replacement of the old by the new takes place under the gardner's very eyes, but is undisclosed to his view until the transition is accomplished. The bafflement, however, is only one of degree, but not of kind; new marigolds may appear in places least suspected, but hardly new oak trees in a marigold bush. The bafflement in the man-made world however, is more often likely to be one of *both degree and kind*. The explosive powers spectacularly ushered over Hiroshima, the zooming into the outer regions of interstellar space, culminating in the precise measurement of phenomena on Venus, 36,000,000 miles away, disclosed new beginnings which bore little resemblance to the roots from which they sprang, of broken metal and burnt gases.

How can these unparalleled achievements be anticipated with any reasonable measure of precision? Without such a guide, careful juggling of funds between "offensive" and "defensive" R&D efforts, and between "existing products" and "new products," can remain as an excuse for exercises in unrelieved ignorance. The "products" should be first technologically feasible; and second, marketable. If something is technologically impossible not only in the light of present but also potential, then no amount of R&D allocations would do the trick. Further, if something is technically feasible — one can in fact make a silk purse out of a sow's ear — it has still to sell before R&D expenditures to make the product are warranted as far as profit-making organisms are concerned.

Thus, we should turn away from "products" considerations to the more basic considerations of technical feasibility. The "products" that are found to be feasible technically have yet to pass the test of marketability, but there is little point in discussing "products" which are technically infeasible.

PERIODIC LAW AND TECHNICAL FEASIBILITY

What "products" are technically feasible?

A similar question was posed in the 1870's. What "elements" are structurally feasible? The ingenuity and skill in formulating the periodic law as a means of discovering elements which should satisfy certain properties solely by reason of structural arrangement, may shed some light on our attempt at an answer to the question: "What products are technically feasible?" In order to learn from the insight of periodic law, we need to consider the major *concept* which formed the building blocks.

> Dmitri I. Mendeléyev discovered in the mid-19th century that the chemical elements show a periodic recurrence of properties when they are arranged in a certain order, which is approximately the order of increasing atomic weight. The statement of this fact, which has been of inestimable value in the development of the

science of chemistry, is called the periodic law; and a tabular arrangement of the elements which brings those with similar properties into juxtaposition is called the periodic table or periodic system of the elements . . . .

The great value of the periodic law was made evident by Mendeléyev's success in 1871 in finding that, by changing 17 elements from the positions indicated by the atomic weights which had been accepted for them into new positions, their properties could be correlated with those of other elements. Menedeléyev was also able to predict the existence of many of the properties of the undiscovered elements eka-boron, eka-aluminum, eka-silicon, eka-manganese, and eka-tantalum, now identified with the elements scandium, gallium, germanium, technetium, rhenium, and protactinium, respectively. Similarly, after the discovery of helium and argon, the periodic law permitted the prediction of the existence of neon, krypton, xenon and radon. . . .

During the development of modern atomic physics and the theory of quantum mechanics, a precise and detailed understanding has been obtained of the electronic structure of the noble gases and other atoms which explains the periodic law in a thoroughly satisfactory manner .

The periodicity of properties of the elements is caused by the periodicity in electronic structure. The noble gases are all chemically unreactive because their electronic structures are stable — their atoms hold their quota of electrons strongly, have no affinity for more electrons, and have no tendency to share electrons with other atoms. An element close to a noble gas in the periodic system, on the other hand, is reactive chemically because of the possibility of assuming the stable electronic configuration of noble gas by losing one or more electrons to another atom, by gaining one or more electrons from another atom, or by sharing electrons . . . .

The properties of elements in the same group of the periodic system are, although similar, not identical. The trend in properties from the lighter to the heavier elements may be attributed to changes in the strength of binding of the outer electrons and especially to the increasing size of the atoms . . . .

This great generalization, the periodic law, which first showed its value through Mendeléyev's prediction of the existence and properties of undiscovered elements, is again being put to the same use; the undiscovered elements of the present interest being those that have greater atomic number than the known elements, and that will be sought not in nature's minerals, but in preparations made by man.[1]

What are the conceptual bases of the periodic law which ensured its

---

[1]Linus C. Pauling, "Periodic Law," *Encyclopaedia Brittanica* (Chicago: 1960), vol. 17, pp. 517, 520-522.

validity as much in the light of the modern electronic structure of matter as in the day of Mendeléyev and the atomic weight?

1. The relationship between atomic weight and nuclear charge. Ernest Rutherford's experiments (1911) on the scattering of alpha particles by the nuclei of heavy atoms led to the observation that the nuclear charge of the electron was roughly one-half the atomic weight.

2. The stability of the paths of the electrons. The Pauli Exclusion Principle states that no more than two electrons can occupy the same orbit (or in wave-mechanical language, orbital) in an atom, and that these two electrons in the same orbital must be paired — that is, must have their spins opposed (1925); the discovery of the spin of the electron by G. E. Uhlenback and S. G. Oudsmit (1925).

3. The probability associated with orbital "jumps" of electrons. Electrons jump from one orbit to another, not continuously, but in quanta of time and energy; the development of quantum mechanics by W. Heisenberg and E. Schrödinger (1925).

4. Electronic theory of valence and molecular structure. The discovery of the shared electron pair by G. N. Lewis in 1916.

Neither the detailed knowledge of the electronic structure of atoms nor the development of quantum mechanics provided the basic insight into periodic law. Its essence was expressed (1862) by A. E. B. de Chancourtois: "The properties of the elements are the properties of numbers." It is the chemical properties of the elements that are determined by the extranuclear electronic structure, and which show the periodicity described in the periodic law, and *not* the properties of the atomic nuclei themselves, such as the magnitude of the packing fraction and the power of entering into nuclear reactions. In other words, the chemical properties are the observable properties of the elements in their relationship with other elements, by themselves, or in combination. These properties may be referred to as the *behavioral properties*. These behavioral properties are correlated with the *external measurement* of the elements themselves, namely, their atomic weight.

How can the observable porperties of the resources available to the organism aid in determining the areas of research which are technologically feasible, so that the organism may not (consistently) waste resources trying, as we have said earlier, to make a silk purse out of a sow's ear? In two ways, which are somewhat parallel to items 1 and 3 above. Rutherford's contribution was in establishing the magnitude of existing capability of the electron; not in adding to it. On the other hand, Heisenberg and Schrödinger showed that the electron could in fact have a change in its capability by means of the orbital "jumps."

The two concepts we shall use are: behavioral properties and structural propensities. The former, like Rutherford's magnitude measurement, establishes the capabilities of the resources available to the organism; which process itself may suggest new directions in which the existing capabilities of the resources could be exploited. The latter, like Heisenberg and Schrödinger's change in the capability of the electron, suggests potential leaps to new planes of capabilities of the resources.

We shall first develop briefly these two concepts, relate them to the organismic objectives considered in Part I, and examine them with reference to real-life examples in as widely varying fields as food and aerospace.

TECHNOMETRIC STRUCTURE

We define *technometric structure* of an organism as comprising its behavioral properties and structural propensities.

BEHAVIORAL PROPERTIES

The classification of behavioral properties calls for creative effort verging on genius. Of the hundreds of behavioral properties that are visible, and of the hundreds that are not visible, which properties provide an appropriate basis for identification of the elements themselves?

Once the hundreds of properties are identified, there remains the question of establishing the structural relationship among the properties themselves. For instance, consider the melting point of metallic elements. Different metallic elements melt at different temperatures, under the same atmospheric pressure. It is one thing to say that melting point is an important behavioral property of metallic elements, but quite another to discover a meaningful pattern among the melting points. For instance, consider the following:

Element	Atomic Weight	Melting Point
Iron	55.85	1535°C
Copper	63.57	1083°C
Platinum	195.23	1773.5°C

Can we say anything about the metals from their behavioral property of melting point? For instance, can we say that the higher the melting point, the higher the atomic weight of the element? It would hold in the case of iron and platinum, whose melting points, respectively, are 1535°C and 1773.5°C, and corresponding atomic weights 55.85 and 195.23. If there is a direct relationship between the melting points and the atomic weights of elements, then the 238.5°C rise in the melting points corresponding to an increase in the atomic weights of 139.38 could be used as a basis to say: Every degree centigrade rise in melting point of an element represents 0.58 increase in the atomic weight. Since such a rule would be based on the end-points, consisting of the elements iron and platinum, this law should hold most closely within the ranges of atomic weights between 56 and 195. Copper, whose atomic weight is known to be 63.57, falls within the range of 56 and 195. Since its atomic weight is 7.72 higher than that of iron, by this rule, the melting point of copper should be 7.72 ÷ 0.58 = 13.31°C higher than that of iron, namely 1548°C. In fact, the melting point of copper is 1083°C, or 452° less than that of iron. Applying this rule, the atomic weight of copper should be 452 × 0.58 = 262.16 less than the atomic weight of iron or − 206.31.

The moral of this exercise is that more than the atomic weights and their melting points is required to establish a meaningful pattern; should there be a meaningful pattern to the melting points, vis-à-vis some other properties, then simply by knowing this behavioral property one is able to place a particular new metallic element among a group of metals with known melting points.

However, in the context of research planning, the important question is not *where* in the family of metals or elements a new entity belongs, but *what* this resource can do, by itself and in combination with the other resources of the organism. The answer to the question: "Where"? is certainly necessary for research planning involving the use of the resource; but is not sufficient: we also need the answer to the question: "What?" These interrelated questions will be further pursued in the section on Technometric Structure and Organismic Objectives, after considering the other concept of change, viz.-structural propensities.

STRUCTURAL PROPENSITIES

Equally important as the behavioral properties of the elements are their *structural propensities*. We may consider the behavioral properties as static measures. These measures reflect changes from time to time as new knowledge is gained and utilized, e.g., metallic type lasted longer than wooden typesetters used in primitive printing. However, a quantum jump in behavioral properties was made when linotyping was invented; molten metal could be cast and recast to provide excellent type. The result was not a mere linear extension of the durability of the type in the changeover from wood to metal; it was a new dimension of functional dexterity. With linotype, there was no tedious setting of types by hand; the operator merely pushed down keys on the special machine and letters were molded instantly. No more need to sort and store the type after use; the type would be thrown into the crucible to make molten metal. Also, no more worry about lost type, which had to be replaced before composing could take place; just strike a key on the lino keyboard and the desired letter was formed. The skills required for the operation changed accordingly — ability to read the types upside down, infinite patience in picking and choosing, acquiring the knowledge of the inventory of types was supplanted largely by the ability required of a good typist — in general, switch from manual to mechanical skills.

Structural propensities are the tendencies on the part of the resources and organisms employing the resources to make quantum jumps in their respective behavioral properties.

Quantum jump was the essence of Edward Teller's remark: "Why use a 1958 warhead on a 1965 weapons system?"

> In the summer of 1957, a Navy study group known as Project NOBSKA developed reasons for recommending the use of ballistic missiles from submarines, but was somewhat appalled by the actual embodiment of the system built about the solid propellant version of JUPITER, utilizing a payload basically intended for ICBM ranges. Edward Teller was a consultant to NOBSKA, and made the simple observation "why use a 1958 warhead in a 1965 weapons system?" He went on to indicate that radically smaller and lighter warheads should be available on a compatible time scale to the submarine development. He could not spell these out in detail, but produced historical evidence of the trends in warhead dimensions which was convincing enough to set the pace of design for what became *Polaris*. Here again, there was much painful and analytical work to be done, including an intensive three months' study of all the weapon systems parameters by government agencies and contractors. But the germ of the whole idea — the thing which turned the FBM from a monster into a weapon (as one eminent consultant remarked) — was in Teller's remark.[2]

"Why use a 1958 warhead in a 1965 weapons system?" is the key to Teller's foresight. Based on the trend towards miniaturization, he developed

---

[2] William F. Whitmore, "Military Operations Research — A Personal Retrospect," *Operations Research* (March-April 1961), vol. 9, no. 2, p. 263.

the correct hypothesis that miniature electronic equipment would be developed and these would permit construction of smaller warheads with greater punch. It was not merely an obstinate belief on the part of Teller which persuaded the Navy that radically smaller and lighter warheads should be available by 1965. Teller produced historical evidence of the trends in warhead dimensions to give credence to the possibility that smaller and lighter warheads should be available. The behavioral properties of the resources involved here would be smallness and lightness of warheads. The structural propensities of the resources involved would be the structural feasibility that a "jump" could be made from liquid to solid propellants.

These quantum jumps change radically the functional dexterity of the organism which employs the resources. Increase in airspeeds made possible by advances in piston engines and jet engines are "linear" extensions, being improvements in the performance capability in airspeed. However, missiles represent a quantum jump because with missiles we no longer talk merely about *how* faster and faster they can go, but about the altogether new dimension of dexterity, including, but not limited to, interstellar explorations heretofore unimaginable and virtually impossible by the extreme extensions of speed in air travel.

The question of allocation of funds to research and development has to face the bigger issue: What is the nature of the particular segment of the outside world toward which the fruits of this research and development are directed? Thus, in order to decide whether or not allocations should be appropriated for work on the RS-70 airplane, the question has to be answered: What will be the most reasonable form of defense or offense in which a plane traveling at a greater speed than that of sound would be usable? However, a question for research and development of color television should answer the question: What is the dimensional nature of home entertainment in the immediate visible future — is the world of color television a world in which it will have to compete with "see-hear-feel," or empathic, entertainment?

While the consumption aspect underscores the consumer in the real world, the technical aspect underscores the *resources and continuing extension of conceptual breakthroughs beyond current resource capabilities*. But if such extension of conceptual breakthroughs is not to be a mere flight of fancy, one should not only have the head in the clouds, but also, simultaneously, the feet firmly planted on the ground. With reference to the organism, the consequence of head being in the clouds would be postulation of events and relationships for tomorrow which are utterly unexpected on the basis of today's functioning alone. The consequence of the feet being firmly planted in the ground in this context will be the careful determination and to a degree, measurement of, both behavioral properties and structural propensities of the resources and the environment in such a way that conceptual breakthroughs are characterized by quantum of breakthroughs, instead of a mere extension of the present functioning levels.

TECHNOMETRIC STRUCTURE AND ORGANISMIC OBJECTIVES

Corresponding to the resources available to each organism, and the objectives of the organism to be accomplished by the manipulation of these resources, there can be identified both the behavioral properties and structural propensities. Measurement of properties of the output of the organism would be governed by the strategic and tactical objectives of the organism itself. The strategic and tactical objectives were discussed earlier (pp. 32-34). In other words, the measurement *qua* measurement is of little consequence in arriving at the behavioral properties and structural propensities germane to the organism. *It is measurement of resources with respect to output of the organism in order to accomplish organismic objectives* that we are concerned about. In the painstaking measurements of the solar system, Kepler undertook the observation of heavenly bodies over a considerable length of time. Before Newton could work on the coordination of these observations to provide a unified explanation of celestial phenomena, there had to be *empirical observations* of behavioral properties of the celestial bodies, namely their appearance at successive points in time-space coordinates. Whether or not these successive appearances at different points were occasioned by forces endogenous to the heavenly bodies themselves, or external to them was a different concern: a concern which was generated by the actual empirical measurement of the behavioral properties. Similarly, the failure of Michelson-Morley experiment to show any difference in the velocity of light relative to the earth's motion in a hypothetical "ether" was another empirical measurement of a behavioral property.

Each organism should undertake empirical measurement of behavioral properties germane to its output. Whether its output involves a system of international inspection via space platforms, or sale of steel seating to industrial organizations, or whether it involves hundreds of chemical products which enter into scores of other outputs, the nature of the output should be established in its relationship with the corresponding inputs.

DIMENSIONS OF DISCOVERY

The technometric structure of the *organism* sets the stage for its evolutionary or revolutionary movements; and the organism's movements are conditioned by the technometric structure of its *basic resources.* Thus the aircraft companies of the 1910's underwent a revolutionary transformation in the 1960's when their outputs changed from aircraft to missiles. Contributing substantially to this transformation of the organisms (aircraft manufacturers) was the quantum jump in behavioral properties of the resources from semimetals — silicon and germanium — to semiconductors.

We identified the behavioral properties of the resources of the organism as the stationary identity of the organismic resources. Perceptible progress is made when there is a quantum jump in the behavioral properties, giving rise to an extension of these properties, or a creation of new properties. How the transition from the stationary to the dynamic status takes place is indicated by the structural propensities of the resources and capabilities.

Thus, when one raises the question; How much for old, and how much for new product research? an underlying dimension which seriously governs the outcome is overlooked. The dimension of properties of resources primarily decides whether anything at all can be done about products, old and/or new. If someone decides that a new headache remedy is needed, and pours money for research on this dream pill, "Deheadacher," he has charged forth without benefit of counsel — on the marketing side, can "Deheadacher" fulfill a need, or create a need and fulfill it; more important, on the technical side, can any combination of resources with known properties deliver the services hoped for in "Deheadacher?"

Existing resources or fresh inventions may provide the properties desired, and existing combinations or new combinations may deliver the services as desired. In either case, intelligent learning is facilitated by our two concepts — Periodic Table of Product Diversification can offer counsel on the marketing side (see pp. 153-154), and technometric structure can offer counsel on the technical side.

The services conceived to be offered by "Deheadacher" may call for (a) extended performance of the properties of current resources, or (b) for the creation of new properties. What is the direction of the properties of these resources? If the present headache pill begins to take effect five minutes after administration and depresses headache pain for twenty minutes, (a) extended performance of properties of current resources might mean that "Deheadacher," the end-product of these properties, will depress headache pain for thirty minutes, and that it will begin to take effect two minutes after administration. On the other hand, (b) resources with new properties might mean that "Deheadacher" will prevent headaches, or waft them away before the potential sufferer even recognizes that the attack has been dispelled.

In technometric language, there is a quantum jump between (a) and (b). It may very well be true that there is no money in "just another headache pill." Depression of headache for twenty, thirty, or fifty minutes may make little difference to the consumer. An "All-Day Headache-Preventer," something which provides protection against headaches, will be a sufficiently revolutionary concept to hold promise of a really big payoff. Technometric structure does not promise the big payoff; it merely provides a framework to understand ideational activity in such a way that *when* and *whether* or not (a) is warranted, or (b) is warranted, or neither is warranted, because substantial outlays are likely to be called for even modest improvements.

The dimensions of discovery may be visualized as the catalyst which enables the organism to make periodic jumps between successive states of the behavioral properties of the organism. Can we hypothesize any general relationship between the technometric structure and the dimensions of discovery?

SIZE, SPEED, TEMPERATURE

The metamorphosis of aircraft industries into missile manufacturers was, it will be recalled, accelerated significantly by the quantum jump in behavioral properties of silicon and germanium from semimetals to semiconductors.

Microminiaturization, essence of the new science of microelectronics, is already outmoding the revolutions wrought by vacuum tubes and transistors. The miracles of microelectronics have grown out of basic research in solid-state physics, which studies the behavior of matter in its *solid* rather than its liquid or gaseous form. The property of limited conductivity of electricity in semiconductor materials like silicon and germanium, which permits the creation of positive and negative regions by selecting and arranging the impurities such as boron and arsenic, has given rise to the group of extremely useful outputs including diodes, transistors, and rectifiers. The art of "growing" impure crystals which will be conductors of electricity at command is still very young. Therefore, the creation of positive and negative regions involving only a few thousand atoms and occupying almost no space at all is the future target when such crystals would be able to do the combined work of many diodes, many transistors, many triple- and quadruple-decker semiconductor sandwiches all at once.

Size

The chief feature of miniaturization is *size*. Advances in microelectronics have encouraged the United States to concentrate on packing more and more power in smaller and smaller packages.

In the meantime, the U.S.S.R. has been concentrating on building bigger and more powerful rocket boosters. Both these developments can be categorized under the same dimension of discovery: *size*. Broadly speaking, we have concentrated on *smaller* and they have concentrated on the *bigger*.

These choices are crucial, because they involve firm commitment of resources over fairly long periods of time. The United States extension of capability in miniaturization contributed to the space-first of measurement of Venus, 36,000,000 miles away. At the same time, the U.S.S.R. extension of capability in rocket boosters contributed to the prolonged team flights in space. In terms of dimensions of discovery, both of us concentrated primarily on size — but with substantially different end-results.

Temperature, Speed

Stimulated in part by the difficulties of crystal growing, the dimension of temperature has been pursued vigorously. Absence of resistance to electricity which occurs in metals in extreme cold is exploited in some microcircuits which are mounted in baths of helium at − 450°F. Computer circuits operating at these low temperatures get speed by operating in extreme cold. The capability of commanding resources at extremely low temperatures has also permitted innovations in the medical field: Parkinson's disease can now be successfully treated at cyrogenic temperatures. Whether the objective of output is power or healing, the distinguishing mark of cryogenics is temperature.

Speed of the computer circuit at extremely low temperatures itself can be considered another dimension of discovery. The current governmental interest in supersonic flights highlights the dimension of speed. The turbojet engines which are used in the subsonic and transonic flights, are basically streamlined tubes with compressor, burners, and turbine. The turbine extracts part of the energy produced by the compression heating within the engine of the cold air which comes in at the front of the engine to drive the compressor, leaving a large volume of expanding and accelerating hot gas at the back end of the engine. This action produces a powerful "push" or "thrust" which is transmitted through the attachment of the engine to the airframe, forcing the airplane forward and creating lift through the wing reaction to the airstream and producing the forward speed of the airplane. The same principle may be applicable in supersonic flights; it may not be. But the dimension of speed has been highlighted by the governmental decision to sponsor supersonic commercial flights.

Size, temperature, speed — these are but three of the multitudes of dimensions of discovery.

The choice of a particular dimension of discovery as the context of continued research for a specified time does not, by any means, "legislate" results in that particular dimension. Since the basic concern is the conversion of matter into energy in different forms, developments in one dimension are nearly always likely to contribute to innovations in other fields. It would seem quite reasonable as a proposition in electrical conductivity that if there are crystals, like diamond, which do not conduct electricity, and other crystals, including most of the metallic ones like copper or silver, that do conduct electricity, there should be some entities which fall in between, namely, those which conduct not all the time, or very well, but some of the time, and somewhat well. But the successful arrangement and selection of impurities in semiconductors explosively ushered in the science of microelectronics in the dimension of size, with reverberations in other dimensions including those of speed (airplanes) and temperature (computer circuits operating in extreme cold).

Additional Instances of Linear Extensions and Quantum Jumps

From the illustrative instances of extension of behavioral properties (e.g., thirty minutes of headache relief instead of the present twenty minutes), and quantum jumps in the behavioral properties (e.g., an "all-day-headache-preventer") we now turn to the detailed application of the concepts to the historical development of well-known industries: food and aerospace. In the case of the former, temperature is the primary dimension of discovery; in the latter, size is the primary dimension of discovery.

The safe period of storage of foods is sought to be extended by the housewife boiling milk in the tropics. The duration is counted in minutes, hours. However, the extension of this behavioral property — linear extension — soon reaches a limit. Refrigeration provides a quantum jump to the period of safe storage of food, from minutes and hours to days and months. A whole new crop of industries sprang up as a result of the quantum jump in the behavioral property.

The results are even more remarkable in the transformation of the aircraft industry into the aerospace industry. Accelerating the transformation ushered in by microminiaturization is the governmental sponsorship of aerospace activities. A much larger crop of new industries than in the case of refrigeration sprang up. What insights do these large-scale and revolutionary changes offer to the systematic inquiry into the technological feasibility of the organism's capabilities to prepare for change?

DIMENSION OF DISCOVERY: TEMPERATURE
TRANSFORMATION OF INDUSTRY: FRESH FRUIT TO FROZEN FOODS

Temperature as a dimension of discovery ushered in revolutionary changes in the national economic life of Europe and America; it even made possible new departures in international trade, bringing millions of eggs from South Africa and elsewhere to Europe in perfect condition after a voyage of a month or six weeks. In its wake new industries were set up and old ones transformed. The beginnings of these innovations were in the behavioral properties of resources — fruits and vegetables, game and fish, milk and meat. As a consequence, radical changes and complete transformations took place in the organisms based on the resources.

STERILIZATION BY HEAT

Temperature is the major dimension of discovery in food preservation. Heat is applied to food to destroy bacteria in order to prevent or deter the process of decay and decomposition. The art of preservation of food developed very slowly over many centuries through purely empirical efforts — drying, smoking, or curing with salt being the principal methods.

> The very fact that a substance is available as food for man presupposes that it is decomposable by living agencies, either microbes or enzymes. If bacteria are completely excluded, foodstuffs will keep indefinitely, so that the problem to be solved is how to destroy all living organisms in the food and prevent their subsequent access .... Of the various methods of preserving food ... only one — sterilization by heat — aims at the complete destruction of all bacterial life.[3]

When the housewife boils milk in the tropics, she is killing the bacteria in it. When she covers the potted meat with a layer of hot fat, or the jam with paper soaked in brandy, she is preventing reinfection of food from which bacteria have been removed.

> Few bacteria can long survive at temperature of about 80°C (176°F). In the presence of moisture (those which can be termed thermophilic) with the exception of some spore formers which

---

[3] H. E. Cox and J. A. Tobey, "Food Preservation," *Encyclopaedia Britannica* (Chicago: 1960), vol. 9, p. 454.

need temperatures as high as 140°C (284°F) for their destruction .... The presence or absence of air is an important factor since
bacteria and their spores are of two classes, aerobes and anaerobes,
which, respectively, grow in the presence or absence of air; of
these, the aerobes are much the larger class, and among its
members are those organisms which are most frequently the cause
of spoilage.[4]

The important principle of sterilization by heat is that the useful
life of food can be extended. Thus, if heat renders food temporarily sterile,
say, for one hour, heating it a second time would probably extend the
period to two hours, and so on. Subsequent cooking can be employed to
keep food for very long periods of time, if adequate means are taken to
prevent reinfection.

Large-scale sterilization processes generally consist of heating the
tins or pots in trays in a large autoclave or pressure chamber, by
means of a superheated steam, to temperatures in the neighborhood
of 120°C (240°F), but vary according to the foodstuff. The time is
also variable, though it should be sufficient to insure that the
central parts of the tins reach at least 100°C (212°F); it therefore
depends upon the size and distribution of the cans in the oven.
After this cooking, the sealed tins are allowed to cool slowly in the
oven with a suitable adjustment of the pressure, or they are
removed and conveyed through tanks of water until a temperature
of about 100°F is reached.[5]

Thus, whether food is preserved by sterilization on a small scale in
the pots by the housewife or on a large scale in autoclaves, the food is preserved in a form different from its original raw state. Thus boiled milk is
edible, *but* has a different taste from fresh milk. The boiled milk is
sterile for a short time, which period can be extended by further heating.

If sterilization is accomplished only through heat, corresponding to
that state of the behavioral properties of the resources, what are the organisms that can be supported? Consider the following industries:

FRUIT: 3522: *Farm machinery and equipment* — establishments primarily engaged in manufacturing farm machinery ...
for use in preparing, on the farm, crops for market.

2033: *Canned fruits, vegetables, preserves, jams and jellies*
— establishments primarily engaged in canning fruits
and vegetables, and fruit and vegetable juices; and in

---

[4] *Ibid*, pp. 454-455.

[5] *Ibid.*, p. 455.

manufacturing catsup and similar tomato sauces, preserves, jams, and jellies.

MILK: 2025: *Special dairy products* — establishments primarily engaged in manufacturing special dairy products, such as processed cheese, cheese food, cheese spread, and malted milk (acidophilus milk).

2026: *Fluid milk* — establishments primarily engaged in processing (pasteurizing, homogenizing, vitaminizing, bottling) and distributing fluid milk and cream, and related products.

MEAT: 2011: *Meat packing plants* — establishments primarily engaged in slaughtering, for their own account or on a contract basis for the trade, of cattle, hogs, sheep, lambs, calves, horses, and other animals except small game, for meat to be sold or to be used on the same premises in canning and curing, and in making sausages, lard, and other products.[6]

STERILIZATION BY REFRIGERATION

While sterilization by heat provided extension of the life of food to, say, hours, and days, sterilization by refrigeration introduced an altogether new dimension into the life span of food articles. The changes in the behavioral properties of the resources — foodstuffs in this instance — are brought about by reducing the temperature to which they are subject so that the activity of any bacteria or enzymes present is suspended. Inhibition of activity of bacteria is preferable to attempts to destroy all bacteria present in foodstuffs, which generally does not succeed because (1) of the unevenness of the heat sterilization, permitting some bacteria in the center of the mass to remain alive, and (2) of the possibility of spores surviving even in conditions under which the bacteria are killed.

The object in refrigeration is not to kill bacteria, since these microscopic forms of life can resist a very low temperature without injury; it is to reduce or arrest completely their activity. Most bacteria are rendered incapable of growth at the freezing point of water, so that at or below this temperature all biological change ceases and the only changes which may go on are physical ones, depending on the evaporation of water and the volatile flavoring substances, or certain chemical oxidation changes. Enzymes also are retarded in their activity by low temperatures. Refrigeration includes both freezing and chilling, not merely because it involves

---

[6] Executive Office of the President, Bureau of the Budget, *Standard Industrial Classification Manual,* (Washington, D.C.: U.S. Government Printing Office, 1957), pp. 47-48, 100.

much lower temperatures but because of its effects on the food itself . . . .

Meats, including game and fish, were the first foods to be frozen for preservation. Dairy products, such as butter and cream, probably followed, except for possible isolated experiments. Work on the freezing of fruits and vegetables started in 1917.[7]

We see from Table III that the safe *storage periods* of foodstuff have undergone a dramatic change in order of magnitude, from *hours* to *months,* when means of sterilization changed from heat to refrigeration.

In addition to the dramatically extended period of safe storage, refrigeration permits the storing of food in the raw (e.g., fresh milk), as opposed to an altered state (e.g., boiled milk).

These advantages of sterilization by refrigeration over that by heat made it possible for enormous quantities of food, meat, fish, fruit, butter, eggs, and vegetables to be exported, imported, and stored under refrigeration. This possibility totally altered the economic life of nations, by making it possible for the abundance of supply in one country to offset the scarcity in another.

Symptomatic of the revolutionary changes in the behavioral properties of organisms — food industries — is the spontaneous expansion of what is known as the locker-plant industry. Plants or concerns devoted to the storing of frozen foods for private use and in relatively small amounts have come to be known in the United States and Canada as locker plants. It is believed that the first locker plants were established in the late 1920's. According to Frederick S. Erdman, the earliest growth of the locker-plant industry in the United States was in the northwest, and from there it spread

TABLE III

SAFE STORAGE PERIODS OF FOODSTUFFS

Foodstuff	Approximate Storage Period (months)		
	At 0°F	At 5°F	At 10°F
Beef, fruit juices	12 to 15	10 to 12	6 to 8
Fruits, vegetables, veal, venison	10 to 12	8 to 10	3 to 6
Lamb, poultry, rabbits, game birds, eggs	8 to 10	6 to 8	3 to 4
Fresh pork, ham, creamery butter, cheese	6 to 8	4 to 6	2 to 3
Ground meat (unsalted), lean fish, cottage cheese	4 to 6	3 to 4	1 to 2
Beef liver, fatty fish, slab bacon, cooked foods	2 to 4	2 to 3	1 to 2

Source: J. D. Winter and A. Hurstrulid, "Freezing Foods for Home Use," *Extension Bulletin 224,* University of Minnesota, revised June 1945.

---

[7] H. E. Cox and J. A. Tobey, "Food Preservation," *Encyclopaedia Britannica* (Chicago: 1960), vol. 9, pp. 454, 456.

to the mountain states and on to the Middle West, where it grew rapidly in the heavy meat-consuming communities. By 1935 there were probably about 250 locker plants of all types; by the close of 1940 the total in the United States had risen to about 2,900; and by the end of 1945 there were 6,850 plants. A survey by the United States Department of Agriculture showed that in 1943 the locker plants in the United States served about 1,500,000 families and handled a turnover of frozen foodstuffs of about 865,000,000 pounds. This represented about 430 pounds of meat and 70 pounds of other foodstuffs, on the average, per locker per year.

In Table IV we find the growth of the frozen food industry in the United States. The dramatic transformations that were brought over the *organisms* (foodstuff industries) as a result of the changes in the behavioral properties of the *resources* (sterilization by refrigeration instead of heat) can be visualized from a sampling of the different industries which would not otherwise have been possible.

TABLE IV

GROWTH OF THE FROZEN FOOD INDUSTRY IN THE UNITED STATES

Foodstuffs Frozen	Millions of Pounds	
	1935	1944
Vegetables	7[1]	233
Fruit	77	313
Sea foods	150	247[2]
Poultry stocks	132	218[3]
Eggs	206	512
Meat stocks	400	500[3]
All foods in locker plants	30[2]	865[4]
Cooked foods	—	—
Total	1,002	2,888

[1] Western states only — no record of pack elsewhere.
[2] Estimated.
[3] 1942 figures.
[4] 1943 figures.
Source: *Western Canner and Packer.*

FRUIT: 2037: *Frozen fruits, fruit juices, vegetables, and specialities* — establishments primarily engaged in quick freezing and cold packing (freezing) fruits, fruit juices, vegetables, and specialities.

2087: *Flavoring extracts and flavoring sirups, not elsewhere classified* — establishments primarily engaged in manufacturing flavoring extracts, sirups, and fruit juices, not elsewhere classified, for soda fountain use or for the manufacture of soft drinks, and colors for bakers' and confectioners' use.

MILK: 2023: *Condensed and evaporated milk* — establishments primarily engaged in manufacturing condensed and evaporated milk, and related products, including ice cream mix and ice milk mix made for sale as such.

2024: *Ice cream and frozen desserts* — establishments primarily engaged in manufacturing ice cream and other frozen desserts.

MEAT: 2013: *Sausages and other prepared meat products* — establishments primarily engaged in manufacturing sausages, cured meats, smoked meats, canned meats, *frozen meats,* other prepared meats, and meat specialities, from purchased carcasses and other materials.

2015: *Poultry and small game dressing and packing, wholesale* — establishments primarily engaged in killing, dressing, packing, and canning poultry, rabbits, and other small game for their own account or on a contract basis for the trade. This industry also includes the drying, *freezing,* and breaking of eggs; not the cleaning, oil treating, packing, and crating of eggs which are classified in wholesale trade.[8] [Italics supplied.]

Without any effort to be comprehensive, the large number of industries comprising hundreds of organisms, that are directly traceable to the quantum jump in the behavioral properties of the resources is impressive. In addition to establishing brand new industries, refrigeration made possible advances in both time and space: e.g., storage of milk over longer periods, shipment of eggs from Africa to Europe. The dimension of discovery is predominantly *temperature.* When increased temperatures were applied to food for sterilization purposes, the life of the foodstuffs could be extended, say *linearly* — from minutes to hours and hours to days. As soon as there was a quantum jump in the properties of the resources, the safe storage period of foods jumped into another dimension, from hours and days to months; transformation took place with regard to the organisms as well; an orbital jump from minutes to months instead of a mere continuance along the orbit of minutes. It became possible to maintain fresh flavor and properties for fairly large periods of time using refrigeration, as opposed to the earlier methods of preserving altered flavors and properties for shorter periods. The dimension of discovery — temperature — transformed the industry figuratively from preserved fruits to frozen foods.

---

[8] *Standard Industrial Classification Manual, op. cit.,* pp. 47-48, 52.

DIMENSION OF DISCOVERY: SIZE
TRANSFORMATION OF INDUSTRY: AIRCRAFT TO AEROSPACE

Size, as a dimension of discovery, probably contributed most to the transformation of man's domain of conquest from atmosphere to space. Orville Wright's heavier-than-air machine, which first flew successfully on December 17, 1903, achieved a speed of approximately 45 miles per hour. General Billy Mitchell set a speed record of 223 miles per hour in 1922; and Colonel Frank Everest flew the X-2 at 1,785 miles per hour in 1956. In the meantime, records were being made and broken in the areas of high-altitude flights and long-duration flights. All efforts of man to conquer atmosphere remain "linear" extensions of resource capabilities — higher, faster, longer flights.

Corresponding to the developments in the behavioral properties of the resources — man's wherewithal to fly — there took place developments in the behavioral properties of the organisms. Air transport was first recognized practical in France in 1910. Ten years later, the first transcontinental mail route was established in the United States between New York and San Francisco. Passenger air transport was popularized after Charles A. Lindbergh's New York-Paris flight in 1927. How popular it became is reflected in the rise of the number of passengers carried: 1,306,365 in 1938; 13,245,728 in 1946.

> The manufacture of Military and commercial Aircraft ranked 41st among American Industries in 1939, with total production of about $250,000,000. Five short years later, after major elements of the Automobile Industry and many others had been drawn into the military aircraft orbit, it had become the greatest industry the world has ever known, with peak production for 1944 reaching the colossal sum of $16,000,000,000. (The peak annual production of the Automobile Industry before the war was approximately $4,000,000,000.)[9]

The dawn of the atomic age in 1945 irrevocably altered the course of aircraft industry. Atomic warheads, and later hydrogen warheads, became the potent weapons of annihilation. In the years immediately following the war, Strategic Air Command was considered the best means to deliver the lethal blows. However, there were further changes in the complexion of the means of delivery.

> There has been much talk of future "push-button" warfare, but its meaning and what its relationship may be to the present

---

[9] George B. Woods, *The Aircraft Manufacturing Industry — Present and Future Prospects* (New York: White, Weld & Co., 1946), Introduction.

Aircraft Industry are not clear to the general public. Much the simplest way to explain "push-button" warfare is to describe the second German "vengeance" weapon, or V-2, because its enormous potentialities are based realistically on actual performance which has already been demonstrated. It is a towering ominous missile 49 feet in length with a diameter of 5 ft. 6 in., carrying a 2,000 lb. warhead and weighing at take-off 13½ tons, of which about 9 tons is fuel. Liquid oxygen and ethyl alcohol constitute this rocket fuel, and burn at terrific heat for the relatively short period of 63 seconds. During this short period, however, maximum thrust is 30 tons, as compared with the V-2's total weight of 13½ tons. The take-off of the V-2 is vertical, it is driven to an estimated altitude of 22 miles during this 63 seconds of thrust, and is accelerated during that period to a speed of 3,400 miles an hour. This is over four times the speed of sound (which is 761 mph at sea level) and six times the speed of our newest jet fighters. Controlled in flight by a "pre-set gyroscopic acceleometer" the V-2 then continues under its momentum on up to an altitude of 60 miles from which it descends in a great arc to its intended target, meanwhile slowing up as it comes back down through the earth's atmosphere due to the fact that friction with the air at these enormous speeds exceeds the pull of gravity. Speed at impact with the target is still about 1,700 miles per hour, or well over twice the speed of sound, so that there is no warning of the missile's approach. Radar tracking would be possible, but the speeds were so great that no known defense had been developed up to the close of the war . . . .

The effect of future "push-button" warfare on the Aircraft Industry will be difficult to appraise, and it is quite possible that there will be a lessening emphasis in the future on the type of airplanes we now know. Not only is it possible that the rates of acceleration, speeds and heats developed at transsonic speeds will be too great for human pilotage, but it is also possible that future aircraft rockets guided by television or radio control with light seeking, heat seeking, or proximity fuses, will be so effective that bombing as we know it in the war will not be possible. The trend, therefore, may be toward bombing and interception of bombers by unmanned aircraft or winged missiles, which might result in a far greater rate of expendability as compared with previous bombers most of which returned to their base after their missions were accomplished. Development contracts for unmanned aircraft and winged missiles have been placed with the Aircraft Manufacturing Industry as it exists today and these companies should continue to lead in that field.[10]

QUANTUM JUMPS IN SIZE: NUCLEAR PHYSICS, MICROELECTRONICS

The success of the Manhattan Project, and the advances in rocketry

---

[10] Ibid., pp. 31-33.

at Peenemunde, Germany, facilitated the quantum jump from aircraft to aerospace. Size was clearly a crucial dimension of discovery, whether we consider the potency of the package carried aboard the *Enola Gay* on August 6, 1945, or the compactness of the carriers and custodians of solar and other sources of energy aloft the Soviet Sputniks and the American Explorers and Vanguards circling the earth; not to mention Telstar linking continents and spanning the oceans in a communication clasp.

Underlying the quantum jump in the organisms from aircraft to aerospace is the quantum jump in the behavioral properties of the resources which made possible the explorations of space instead of the atmosphere. This capability is rightly characterized as a quantum jump since more than mere linear extensions of flight — faster, higher, longer — are involved. A whole new dimension of capabilities has been unfolded. The distance that we seek to annihilate is no longer the mundane miles, made up of furlongs, yards, feet and inches, but *light-years* — the distance light travels a year at the rate of 186,284 miles each second, or, 5,880,000,000,000 (5.88 trillion) miles. Earth is 8 light-minutes from the sun: the sunlight travels the 93,000,000 miles from the sun to the earth in that time.

Travel to the moon, which is 239,000 miles away, is but a short trip — 1.285 light-seconds. Our goal is to land a man on the moon within the decade toward which goal the docking in space of two spacecrafts on March 16, 1966 contributed a decisive forward step. We have already been able to make measurements of Venus, 36,000,000 miles away, which indicate that members of the system of stars with our sun as center — solar galaxy — are accessible to us. It may be some time before we shall have explored our own galaxy since light from our sun must travel some 26,080 years to reach the center of our own galaxy, traveling at 186,000 miles per second. Intergalactic explorations are no longer mere science fiction: Teller speculates that, given a space vehicle capable of speeds very near to that of light, an earth spaceman could travel to points a million light-years distant and return — all within his lifetime!

The quantum jumps aiding the transformation of industry, it was observed, relate to both the packaging and amplification of sources of energy. The sources of energy for space travel are three: chemical, solar, and controlled nuclear. Amplification of current is extremely helpful to space explorations, and if these amplifications can be accomplished by means of minute devices, that would lead to providing more bounce to the ounce or punch to the inch. Tiny devices which switch, amplify, and alter electric currents just as vacuum tubes, but equaling a dozen tubes and yards of wiring, and occupying infinitesimal space, ushered in a revolution over a whole range of industries — missiles, airplanes, computers. A small computer has 1,000 or more transistors and several times as many diodes in its anatomy; a really big one may contain several hundred thousand such devices. A single missile may carry as many as 6,000 transistors, and its control equipment may contain tens of thousands more. New airplanes have more and more electronic gear — 100,000 pieces in the B-58 compared to 2,000 in the B-29.

BEYOND ATMOSPHERE, ROCKETS WITH FUEL AND OXIDIZER

Some of the quantum jumps aiding the transformation of aircraft industries into aerospace industries resulted from the very structure of atmosphere and space.

For every action there is equal and opposite reaction (Isaac Newton: 1686). This is the fundamental principle on which all propulsion is based — propeller, jet, or rocket. The propeller aerodynamically transfers the energy of the engine to the surrounding air. The jet does it thermodynamically, by scooping in air, compressing it, heating it by burning fuel, and ejecting the heated air and exhaust gases. Either way, the forward thrust is obtained by accelerating air rearward. But in space there is no air, hence no medium. The engine has no air to breathe to oxidize the fuel. And there is no air to "push against."

As a result, for space travel, man must return to an ancient propulsive device — the rocket. The rocket can breathe in space because it carries its own air with it, so to speak. That is, it contains both fuel and oxidizer. It can propel a vehicle through space because it develops its propulsion solely through reaction, in accordance with Newton's third law, rather than "pushing." Dr. Robert H. Goddard, American rocket pioneer, demonstrated this fact experimentally as early as 1919 . . . .

A rocket fired from earth has to fight its way through the drag of the atmosphere, and has to overcome the very considerable force of gravity. If a rocket is fired straight up, gravity alone will slow it twenty miles an hour every second. Add thermodynamic drag, and final velocity can be cut to around seventy percent. As a result, enormous initial thrust is required . . . .

Basically, a satellite is put into orbit by accelerating it to somewhere above 18,000 miles an hour but less than 25,000 miles an hour (at which speed, the vehicle would be able to overcome earth's gravitational force). This range of speed is known as orbital velocity. That is, the satellite is projected far enough and out at a fast enough speed so that earth's gravity does not pull it back. Yet its velocity is not great enough to release it from earth's gravity and cause it to fly on out into space until it is picked up by the gravitational pull of some other body, such as the moon.

Like many another technological advance, the rocket art was

accelerated by the impetus of military needs . . . . The quickest way to get a hydrogen warhead from one point on the earth's surface to another as much as 5,000 miles away is via space. Thus, the military requirement for long-range ballistic missiles has led to development of engines powerful enough to send payloads into space.[11]

A major end-result of the changes in the resources which extended the capability of resources at the command of the aircraft industry has been to generate the aerospace industry.

The year 1960 saw the aircraft industry move nearer to becoming the "aerospace" industry . . . . The trend toward low-volume, high-precision production, started several years earlier, continued during 1960. This change was dictated by greater emphasis on the guided missile, new military tactics emphasizing high-unit firepower rather than mass-formation techniques, and the cost of complex new aircraft and missiles which made volume production impossible within budget limits . . . .

Manufacture of manned arcraft still constituted in 1960 the major portion of the aircraft industry's workload, although the gap between missiles and aircraft production was again narrowed, as it has been over several years . . . .

Aerospace Industries Association estimated the total U.S. production of aircraft in the calendar year 1960 at slightly more than 10,000 units, a major drop from 1959 production . . . .

Missiles sales took up the slack in declining military aircraft production (by several hundred units to 2,000 in 1960). Missile volume for 1960 was expected to near $4,000,000,000 up from

TABLE V

AEROSPACE INDUSTRY, 1960–1962

	1960	1961	1962
Total sales ($ mil)	11,500	14,873	15,000
Government ($ mil)		11,501*	
Private ($ mil)		3,372*	
Profit margin (percent)	1.4	1.8	2.0
Aircraft products (units)	10,000	9,200	8,500
Aircraft and components as percent of industry volume	60	56	50
Missile-spacecraft as percent of industry volume	40	44	50

Sources: James J. Haggerty, "Aircraft Industry," *Encyclopaedia Britannica, Book of the Year* (Chicago 1961), p. 32; 1962, p.15; 1963, p. 124.

The New York Times, April 29, 1962, p. 1.

[11] The Editors of *Air Force Magazine, Space Weapons* (New York: Frederick A. Praeger, Inc., 1959), pp. 36-37, 39.

$3,500,000,00 in 1959. Military aircraft sales dropped in about the same proportion, from $7,900,000,000 in 1959 to less than $7,400,000,000 in 1960. Although large airline transports cost as much as $6,000,000 each, the great majority of civil aircraft (more than 8,000 units in 1960 compared with 8,242 in 1959) were in the $20,000-$50,000 category; thus the percentage contribution of civil aircraft production to the total volume was relatively small.

The industry's profit margin dropped to a new low of 1.5% of sales. A major contributing factor was the need to divert company funds to build facilities for the new products of the space age. Another factor was the increasing emphasis on research and development work for complex new equipment; research contracts traditionally yield small or no profits, and in some cases losses.[12]

The transformation from aircraft to aerospace is reflected in Table V. The wartime high of $16,000,000,000 of aircraft manufacturing industry sales in 1944 dwindled to $1,000,000,000 in 1946.[13]

According to Aerospace Industries Association spokesmen, quoted just above, the aircraft industry moved nearer to becoming the aerospace industry in 1960, with total sales $11,500,000,000, of which aircraft and components accounted for 60 percent. In the succeeding years, this fraction dropped to 56 percent (1961) and 50 percent (1962). Missile-spacecraft accounted for the remainder, viz; 40, 44, and 50 percent respectively in 1960, 1961, and 1962.

GOVERNMENT PURCHASES AND ACCENT ON SPACECRAFT, ELECTRONICS

Hitler's decision at Peenemunde in early June 1943 to abandon the search for the atomic bomb and concentrate on rockets and the simultaneous decision by Roosevelt and Churchill to search for the atomic bomb represent the political directives that were responsible for the present-day transformation of the aircraft industry into the aerospace industry. This aspect of government directives and sponsorship is very much in evidence today in the aerospace industry.

The aerospace industry, for instance, depends heavily on defense business — to the extent of about 80 per cent of its volume. In 1961, sales of aircraft, space vehicles, missiles and components to the Government alone amounted to $11,501,000,000. By contrast, other customers accounted for $3,372,000,000 in sales . . . .

12 James J. Haggerty, "Aircraft Industry," *Encyclopaedia Britannica Book of the Year* 1961 (Chicago: 1961), p. 32.

13 George B. Woods, *op. cit.,* p. 4.

In the present fiscal year purchases by the Pentagon of space, military and other electronic gear and services are estimated by the Electronic Industries Association at $7,800,000,000. In Fiscal 1963 this figure is expected to rise to about $9,000,000,000 and account for 55 per cent of the total sales of the electronic industry. Ten years ago Government expenditures for electronics were less than one-eighth that amount. The electronics content of the defense budget has risen from 7 to 17.5 per cent.

In the present fiscal year prime defense contracts awarded will amount to some $29,000,000,000 a peacetime record by far.[14]

The heavy role of the government as consumer may be taken as a vantage point to observe the transformation of the aircraft industry into the aerospace industry. Size, as the dimension of discovery, hinges on electronics. As many of the leaders in the aircraft industry exchanged their wings for wingless flight, the tiny devices largely responsible for more punch to the inch began to assume an increasingly important role in what was once the aricraft industry. For instance, we see from Table VI that North American Aviation produced $28 million worth of aircraft in 1939, and $684 million worth of aircraft in 1944. It is one of the top five defense prime contractors, receiving 4.0 percent of the total prime contracts awarded in 1957-61, worth $4,271,000,000. It also has a sizable electronics production, the revenue in 1959 from electronic products being $250,000,000.

The advent of the Space Age, it is apparent, has brought about a sharp shift in the pattern of defense spending. In the fiscal year that ended June 30, 1956, almost 33 per cent of the Defense Department's prime contract awards went for manned aircraft, against 5.6 per cent for missiles. By fiscal 1961, missiles accounted for 25.6 per cent of military spending, aircraft only 21.5 per cent. Electronic equipment of various kinds accounted for 13.7 per cent of prime contract awards.[15]

Curtiss-Wright was the largest aircraft manufacturer with a production of $1,717,000,000 in 1944, but became the 28th defense supplier with 0.6 percent of 1957-61 contracts, worth $613,000,000.

The New York Stock Exchange made a study of the 50 largest defense suppliers listed on the Big Board. According to the study, these 50 obtained 65.4 percent of the prime contracts in fiscal 1961, as compared with 57.1 percent in 1957. A five-year analysis disclosed that these concerns accounted for almost $67,000,000,000, or 62.5 percent of all

---

[14] Richard Rutter, "Defense is the Biggest Business: Pattern Shifts on West Coast," *New York Times* (Apr. 29, 1962), pp. 1, 14.

[15] *Ibid.*, p. 14.

TABLE VI

TRANSFORMATION OF ORGANISM: AIRCRAFT TO AEROSPACE

ORGANISM	AEROSPACE[a,t]		GROWTH OF AIRCRAFT[b]		ELECTRONICS[c]	GROWTH OF AEROSPACE[a]				
						Prime Contracts Annually§ (millions)				
	Total Prime Contracts 1957–1961 (millions)	Percent of all Prime Contracts 1957–1961	Aircraft Production 1939 (millions)	Aircraft Production 1944 (millions)	Electronic Products Revenue 1959 (millions)	1957	1958	1959	1960	1961
	Rank 1									
1. General Dynamics	$7,199	6.7				$1,019	$1,383	$1,616	$1,260	$1,920
2. Boeing	6,133	5.7	12	608		907	2,131	1,167	1,009	920
3. Lockheed Aircraft	4,435	4.1	35	602		536	755	899	1,071	1,175
4. General Electric	4,412	4.1			1,000	877	783	914	963	875
5. North American Aviation	4,271	4.0	28	684	250	500	648	1,018	908	1,197
SUBTOTAL		24.6								
6. United Aircraft	3,048	2.8	52	744		706	661	538	517	626
7. American Telephone & Telegraph	2,746	2.6				592	660	477	467	551
8. Martin-Marietta*	2,579	2.4	24	533		366	400	524	597	692
9. Douglas Aircraft	2,151	2.0	28	1,061		249	513	676	405	307
10. Sperry Rand	1,692	1.6			645	215	370	403	296	408
11. IBM	1,576	1.5			560	362	317	277	290	330
12. Raytheon	1,475	1.4			495	218	237	393	323	305
13. McDonnell Aircraft	1,464	1.4				294	352	404	195	220
14. R.C.A.	1,420	1.3			1,045 Rank 1	133	288	200	405	392
15. Republic Aviation	1,296	1.2	<1	370		190	265	281	265	296
16. Westinghouse Electric	1,255	1.2			260	182	269	238	258	308
17. General Motors	1,251	1.2			280	259	281	211	219	282
18. Bendix Corporation	1,236	1.2				251	208	271	239	267
19. Chrysler	1,026	1.0				99	259	323	187	158
20. Grumman Aircraft	1,023	1.0	4	324		—	245	300	239	238
21. General Tire and Rubber	996	0.9				96	160	207	243	290

TABLE VI (Continued)
TRANSFORMATION OF ORGANISM: AIRCRAFT TO AEROSPACE

ORGANISM	AEROSPACE[ad] Total Prime Contracts 1957–1961 (millions)	Percent of all Prime Contracts 1957–1961	GROWTH OF AIRCRAFT[b] Aircraft Production 1939 (millions)	Aircraft Production 1944 (millions)	ELECTRONICS[c] Electronic Products Revenue 1959 (millions)	GROWTH OF AEROSPACE[a] Prime Contracts Annually[§] 1957	1958	1959 (millions)	1960	1961
22. Northrop	$931	0.9		88		207	284	145	140	156
SUBTOTAL		50.2								
26. International Telephone & Telegraph	723	0.7			305	97	97	139	189	202
28. Curtiss-Wright	613	0.6	49	1,717 Rank 1		195	211	67	70	70
31. Burroughs	495	0.5			175	66	72	121	125	112
34. Philco[†]	434	0.4			285	58	66	96	95	119
35. Ford Motor	427	0.4				69	157	89	31	81
38. Minneapolis-Honeywell	408	0.4			190	74	47	105	98	86
39. Thompson Ramo Woolridge	400	0.4			165	36	64	103	121	77
44. General Precision	327	0.3			155	48	53	73	72	81
46. Bell Intercontinental[‡]	318	0.3	<1		317	119	82	56	61	00
Table Total	57,760[||]	54.2	234	7,048	5,810	9,020	12,318	12,331	11,784	12,741
U.S. Total	107,000	100.0	250	16,000	10,000					

a New York Stock Exchange, The Exchange, April, 1962.

b George B. Woods, *The Aircraft Manufacturing Industry — Present and Future Prospects.* (New York; White, Weld & Co., 1946), p. 3.

c Charles E. Silverman, "The Comings Shakeout in Electronics," *Fortune,* August, 1960, page 120.

d Responsibilities of principal contractors active in Project Apollo (man-on-moon):

2. Boeing — First stage of advanced Saturn C-5 booster
3. Lockheed Aircraft — Escape motor
4. General Electric — Systems-integration reliability
5. North American Aviation — Command and service modules
6. United Aircraft — Fuel cells power source
7. American Telephone & Telegraph — Systems engineering support
9. Douglas Aircraft — S-IVB upper stage of Advanced Saturn booster
10. Sperry Rand — Accelerometers

12. Raytheon — Guidance computer
17. General Motors — Inertial platform
19. Chrysler — First stage of Saturn C-1 booster
22. Northrop — Parachute landing system
38. Minneapolis-Honeywell — Stability and flight-control system

* Glen L. Martin Company (incorporated 1917) became Martin-Marietta Corporation in 1961.
† Philco became a subsidiary of Ford Motor in December 1961.
‡ Formerly Bell Aircraft Corporation, sold defense business to Textron, Inc., in July, 1960.
§ Fiscal years ended June 30.
|| The difference between the total prime contracts for 1957–61 of $57,760 million and the total of annual prime contracts for the years 1957, 1958, 1959, 1960, and 1961 which come out at $58,194 million is 0.75 percent of the 1957–61 figure; and is presumably due to the accounting reporting practices for fiscal periods; and the rounding error in five individual years being larger than the 5-year period as a whole.

Prime contractors holding in-between ranks omitted.

Defense Department contract awards from fiscal 1957 through fiscal 1961.

In Table VI, we have selected from among these 50 leaders in defense supplies companies which were leaders in the aircraft production during World War II, and are current leaders in electronics production. (This general rule has been broken to provide a better picture of the principal contractors themselves.) Thus, Boeing obtained 5.7 percent of the total prime contracts in 1957–61, worth $6,133,000,000. It produced $12,000,000 worth of aircraft in 1939, and $608,000,000 worth in 1944. The electronic products do not constitute an important source of revenue to the company. Radio Corporation of America, on the other hand, was not an aircraft producer of significance during World War II, but emerged with the first rank, with $1,045,000,000 in electronic products revenue in 1959. Its share of total prime contracts during 1957–61 was 1.3 percent, representing $1,420,000,000.

We see that the top five contractors — General Dynamics, Boeing, Lockheed Aircraft, General Electric, and North American Aviation — obtained 24.6 percent of the total contracts for 1957–61. It took the next 17 large prime contractors to represent an additional 25 percent of the prime contracts for 1957–61. The total entries in the Table represent 54 percent of the total prime contracts for 1957–61, 44 percent of the wartime peak aircraft production, and 58 percent of the electronic products revenue in 1959.

TRANSFORMATION OF ORGANISMS AND SIC

Organisms were transformed, and, with them, the industries of which the organisms were components. These changes soon became substantial enough to alter the existing Standard Industrial Classification, and are strikingly reflected in the successive SIC of 1945, 1957, and the 1963 Supplement.

SIC, 1945[16]

> 1929: *Ammunition, not elsewhere classified* — establishments primarily engaged in manufacturing ammunition, not elsewhere classified, including bombs, mines, torpedoes, grenades, depth charges, and chemical-warfare projectiles and their component parts.
>
> 3662: *Radio tubes* — establishments primarily engaged in manufacturing radio receiving and transmitting tubes.

---

[16] Executive Office of the President, Bureau of the Budget, *Standard Industrial Classification Manual, Vol. I: Part 1* (Washington, D. C.: U.S. Government Printing office, 1945), pp. 5, 64, 66.

3722:   *Aircraft engines and engine parts* — establishments primarily engaged in manufacturing aircraft engines and engine parts, but not engaged in manufacturing or assembling complete aircraft. Important products of this industry include internal combustion and jet-propulsion engines; engine mount parts; air scoops; turbo superchargers; lubricating, cooling, and exhaust systems; nonelectric starters; and aircraft engine pumps.

3729:   *Aircraft parts and auxiliary equipment, not elsewhere classified* — establishments primarily engaged in manufacturing aircraft parts and auxiliary equipment, not elsewhere classified, but not engaged in assembling complete aircraft. Important products of this industry include airframe assemblies, wing assemblies, flaps and dive brakes, elevators, fins, rudders, and other empennage assemblies, and alighting assemblies and parts such as landing and beaching gear, pontoons, and landing skis; auxiliary equipment such as deicing equipment, bomb racks, turrets and turret drives, parachutes, targets, link trainers, and other auxiliary equipment especially adapted for aircraft.

Establishments primarily engaged in manufacturing or assembling complete aircraft are classified in Industry 3721, aircraft engines and parts in Industry 3722, propellers and propeller parts in Industry 3723, aeronautical equipment in Industry 3811, and aeronautical electrical equipment in Industry 3641.

SIC, 1957[17]

1929:   *Ammunition, not elsewhere classified* — establishments primarily engaged in manufacturing ammunition, not elsewhere classified, including bombs, mines, torpedoes, grenades, depth charges, chemical warfare projectiles and their component parts.

3662:   *Radio and television transmitting, signaling, and detection equipment and apparatus* — establishments primarily engaged in manufacturing (1) radio and television broadcasting equipment; (2) electric communication equipment and parts, except telephone and telegraph; (3) electronic field detection apparatus, light and heat emission operating apparatus, object detection apparatus and navigational electronic equipment, and aircraft and missile control systems; and (4) other electric and electronic communication and signaling products, not elsewhere classified. Establishments primarily engaged in manufacturing transmitting tubes are classified in Industry 3673.

---

[17] Executive Office of the President, Bureau of the Budget, *Standard Industrial Classification Manual,* (Washington, D.C.: U.S. Government Printing Office, 1957), pp. 45, 110-111, 113.

367: ELECTRONIC COMPONENTS AND ACCESSORIES

3671:   *Radio and television receivingtype electron tubes, except cathode ray* — establishments primarily engaged in manufacturing radio and television receivingtype electron tubes, except cathode ray tubes.

3672:   *Cathode ray picture tubes* — establishments primarily engaged in manufacturing television receivingtype cathode ray tubes.

3673:   *Transmitting, industrial, and special purpose electron tubes* — establishments primarily engaged in manufacturing transmitting, industrial, and special purpose electron tubes.

3679:   *Electronic components and accessories, not elsewhere classified* — establishments primarily engaged in manufacturing specialty resistors for electronic end products; solid state electronic devices and similar devices; inductors, electronic transformers, and capacitors; and other electronic components, not elsewhere classified.

372: AIRCRAFT AND PARTS

3722:   *Aircraft engines and engine parts* — establishments primarily engaged in manufacturing aircraft propellers and propellers and propeller parts.

3729:   *Aircraft parts and auxiliary equipment, not elsewhere classified* — establishments primarily engaged in manufacturing aircraft parts and auxiliary equipment, not elsewhere classified. Establishments primarily engaged in manufacturing or assembling complete aircraft are classified in Industry 3721, aircraft engines and parts in Industry 3722, propellers and propeller parts in Industry 3723, aeronautical instruments in Industry 3811, and aeronautical equipment in Industry 3694.

1963 SUPPLEMENT TO SIC[18]

1925:   *Guided missiles and space vehicles, completely assembled* — establishments primarily engaged in manufacturing completely assembled guided missiles and space vehicles. Establishments primarily engaged in manufacturing guided missile and space vehicle engines and engine parts are classified in Industry 3722; space satellites, guided missiles, and space vehicle airborne and ground guidance, check-out and launch electronic systems and components in Industry

---

[18] Executive Office of the President, Bureau of the Budget, *Supplement to 1957 Edition Standard Industrial Classification Manual*, (Washington, D.C.: U.S. Government Printing Office, 1963), pp. 5-6.

3662; and guided missile and space vehicle airframes, nose cones, and space capsules in Industry 3729.

(Previously part of Industry 1929.)

3674: *Semiconductor (solid state) and related devices* — establishments primarily engaged in manufacturing semiconductor (solid state) and related devices, such as semiconductor diodes and stacks, including rectifiers; transisters; solar cells; and light-sensitive semiconductor (solid state) devices.

(Previously part of Industry 3679.)

The implications of the transformation of organisms for the Industries which comprise such organisms are obvious. Bombs, mines, torpedoes, grenades, depth charges, and chemical-warfare projectiles and their component parts did *not* qualify for a separate industry classification in 1945 or in 1957; hence they were lumped together under the catch-all category 1929 — ammunition, not elsewhere classified — subsumed in which were also missiles and space vehicles. In the 1963 Supplement, a new industry was carved out of Industry 1929, viz.: guided missiles and space vehicles, completely assembled, which came into its own as an industry. It should be noted that as late as 1957, this group did not merit an industry number. Thus, Industry 1925 is a definite, tangible evidence of the transformation of industry that took place as a result of discovery, predominantly in the dimension of size.

In the Standard Industrial Classification in 1945, electronics were conspicuous by their absence in retrospect. Twelve years later, a whole *Industry Group, 367* — electronic components and accessories — was added to SIC. To indicate the fast tempo of developments in this *Industry Group, 367*, we may cite the addition of a *new industry, 3674* — semiconductor (solid state) and related devices — which was added in 1963 in the

TABLE VII

COMPOSITION OF NEW INDUSTRY

New Industry Number	Establishments, Number		Number of employees	Adjusted value Added by Manufacture ($1,000)
	Total	20 or more employees		
3671	85	41	36,968	285,799
3672	75	30	8,554	67,472
3673	48	44	20,146	165,803
3679	1,479	737	132,242	914,811
3729	1,201	508	213,500	1,797,203

Source: *1958 Census of Manufacturers, Vol. II: Industry Statistics, Part 2: General Summary and Major Groups 29 to 39* (Washington, D. C.; U.S. Government Printing Office, 1961), pp. 36D-8, 37B-5.

Supplement to the 1957 Edition of SIC. Table VII reflects the magnitude of the transformation of major organisms.

BLOOD, SWEAT, TOIL, AND TEARS OF TRANSFORMATION

These new shoots and beginnings are no abstraction. They are direct and traceable results of achievements on one or several fronts of the dimensions of discovery. Insofar as human beings are involved in generating, mediating, and implementing the transformations made possible by the quantum jumps in the behavioral properties of resources, corresponding to each achievement in the dimension of discovery, there are also likely to be afflictions in the dimensions of misery.

> Defense industry [which] conjures up to many people a picture of guns and planes rolling off mass-production lines . . . has shifted in its essence from hardware to brains. Rockets and even jet planes are to a great degree custom-tailored rather than assembly-line products. The industry consists basically neither of factories nor machines, but of clusters of organized talent, divided principally into the twin fields of research and management.
>
> The talent teams may deal one day with problems of astronauts' digestion; the next, with labor trouble at a missile base. How thick a rocket's skin should be is no longer a job for a machinist with calipers; it's a matter of coordinating knowledge from a dozen fields, from aerodynamics to metallurgy, and perhaps even espionage. . . .
>
> Last Sunday's [April 22, 1962] Los Angeles Times carried twenty pages of help-wanted advertisements from most of the big companies in the defense business. But they weren't for Rosie the Riveter. They were mostly for Egbert the Engineer — servo systems engineers, reliability engineers, thermodynamics engineers, propulsion engineers, and a score of other categories.[19]

There is general agreement that this trend is going to continue; the trend towards increasing employment of technical personnel and declining production jobs. The reason is that the national military effort calls for highly complicated weapons systems, spacecraft and related equipment; and these can best be provided by Egbert the Engineer. Further, the infinitesimally small devices which have in part mediated the revolutionary change from guns and howitzers to missiles and satellites, have also brought in their trail, mechanical means of performing tasks at extremes of temperatures, each one of which can make obsolete scores of Rosie the Riveters.

---

[19] Gladwin Hill, "Defense is the Biggest Business; Pattern Shifts on West Coast," *New York Times* (Apr. 29, 1962), p. 1.

DEVELOPMENT OF VERSATILE CAPABILITIES

The inevitable changes consequent on the advances in the different dimensions of discovery affect not only the human resources that are participating in the activity of the organism but also the organisms themselves.

> The giant aircraft plants of Republic at Farmingdale and of General Dynamics at Fort Worth employ 15,000 workers each. Extensive lay-offs are foreseen at both plants as their aircraft production is gradually eliminated.
>
> Republic's major product, the F-105 Thunderchief fighter-bomber, is being phased out in 1964, two years ahead of schedule under Department of Defense order. No major replacement work is at hand.
>
> For Republic, which ranks as the nation's sixteenth largest defense contractor, the F-105 accounts for 90 percent of its sales, which amounted to $354,565,000 last year. Thus, the phase-out of the plane poses a substantial adjustment problem for the corporation.
>
> The company is now trying to make the transition from an aircraft company to a space-flight concern.[20]

The old order changeth, yielding place to the new, and old outputs are replaced by new. This process is time-honored. The magnitudes involved are, however, unprecedented. Whether it be the phase-out of the F-105 fighter-bomber for Republic Aviation, or the phase-out of the B-58 supersonic bomber for General Dynamics Corporation, the basic issue is that of identifying ahead of time, as accurately as possible, the profile of changes that are in the wind. In this connection, the concept of quantum jump in the behavioral properties of resources is helpful. However, to the extent that the wherewithal of national security tends to be more and more custom-made, outlining of anticipated changes will have to be looked at in greater detail, and with larger provision for deviations.

One way of looking at the disposition of the resources available to the organism, in order to meet changing circumstances, is to consider the organism in terms of its *technical and manpower capabilities,* instead of skills for specific projects. The *versatility* of the capabilities of the organism would, in large measure, determine its ability to withstand fluctuating demands for different types of capabilities at different times. The long-range planning function of the organism would thus properly be the realistic construction of future profile of demands for the capabilities of the

---

[20] John M. Lee "Pentagon Moves Cause Woes for Two Big Aircraft Companies," *New York Times* (Apr. 29, 1962), p. 14.

organism, and the appropriate deployment of the capabilities to meet such demands.

In other words, the aircraft companies which were pressed into active service, reaching a peak level of performance in 1944, should have considered their stock-in-trade to be *not* airplane production capabilities, but *translocation* of mass. In view of the crucial role the aircraft palyed in the war that was just over, it would have been possible to conceive continuing its important contribution in the military defenses of the nation. Even if the great potential of space exploration were not apparent at that time — although Walter Dornberger makes the statement in his book *V-2*: "We have led our generation to the threshold of space — the road to the stars is now open," referring to the first successful flight of a V-2 missile from the German facility which he commanded at Peenemunde during World War II— the existence of the Space Age should have been recognized by the end of its first year, on October 3, 1958. The evaluation of the capabilities of the aircraft firm should be made in terms of the immediately possible development of the importance of the Space Age. To the extent the capabilities of aircraft production could be deployed, or exchanged at or near par, for capabilities in the spacecraft, to that extent the organism had insured its survival in the changing technological era.

Delightful task! to rear the tender thought,
To teach the young idea how to shoot . . .

JAMES THOMSON, *The Seasons*

CHAPTER FOUR

FROM IDEA TO OUTPUT: PROCESSES, DECISIONS

It is said that there is one thing stronger than all the armies in the world and that is an idea whose time has come. Such a timing presupposes a confluence of several events and relationships, external as well as internal to the organism.

Externally, the idea should belong to a class of ideas which are realizable. Conditions for realizing the idea should be ripe at the particular time and place.

Internally, in order for the potentially realizable idea to be translated into a practical accomplishment, the idea has to make a perilous journey through management decisions.

The technological feasibility basis of research planning, discussed in Chapter 3, has underscored the beginnings of the *external* conditions for fruition of idea. Taking a leaf from the periodic law of the elements, we asked ourselves the question: "How can dimensions of discovery be identified?" We termed the chemical properties and physical properties of the elements, which are observable properties evidenced in their relationship with other elements, by themselves, or in combination, *behavioral properties*. We noted that there are tendencies on the part of the resources, and organisms employing the resources, to make quantum jumps in their respective behavioral properties, which tendencies we termed *structural propensities*.

Dimensions of discovery are the broad areas of investigation of potential quantum jumps in the resources, leading possibly to transformation of organisms employing these resources. And we found historic evidence for the transformation of organisms brought about by the dimensions of discovery, temperature and size, in business as well as military evironments.

What directions should dimensions of discovery take in order effectively to realize their potentials? Can technological history indicate any discernible pattern to the process of discovery? Should such a pattern be identifiable, then, that would provide the *external* setting for the discussion of the necessary *internal* decisions for the realization by the organism of the vast potentials.

AXIS OF DISCOVERY AND LOCUS OF REALIZATION: EXTERNAL GREENLIGHT

Ideational activity is represented in Figure 6 by means of a spinning sphere. Spin could take place in one or more of several directions. These directions are illustrated by the dimensions of discovery listed. Even when one of the dimensions is chosen for investigation, there are variations in direction. Thus, corresponding to the dimension of size, we considered the choice of the United States to explore *smaller* size, while the U.S.S.R. explored *larger* size — smaller electronic equipment and larger rocket boosters.

INHERENT CAPABILITIES AND PROPELLANT EXPLORATIONS

The spin of the sphere itself may be considered the result of the perpetual tension between *inherent capabilities* and *propellant explorations*. The propellant forces tend to move in one direction, and the inherent forces in the opposite direction.

Consider the conversion of matter into energy. Einstein identified

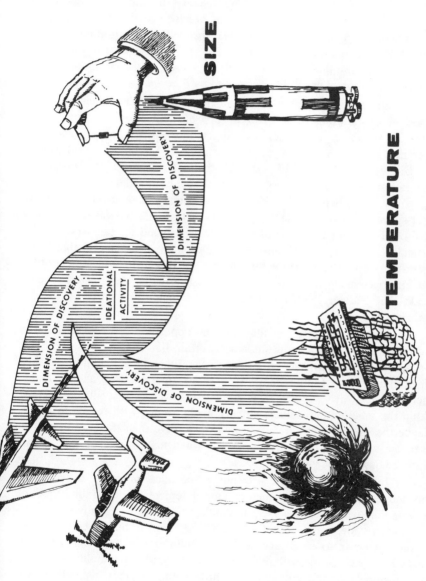

Figure 6. IDEATIONAL ACTIVITY WITH DIMENSIONS OF DISCOVERY.

the inherent *capability* in his equation $E = mc^2$. It also set the *limit* to the amount of energy that is matter. The velocity of light is an absolute in Einstein's relativity; which absolute gives precise meaning to the quantitative content of energy in matter. The propellant explorations, in this connection, are the attempts to release the energy contained in matter. No matter how intense the efforts to unlock the secrets of the atom, there is the inherent limitation of capabilities specified by $E = mc^2$.

Similarly, the great efforts at air travel which began their successful period of explorations after 1903 were propellant efforts successively to travel at subsonic, transonic, and supersonic speeds. Here again, the inherent capabilities have a definite limitation. No object can travel at speeds greater than that of light. If this were not so, the propellant explorations in the dimension of speed could continue indefinitely.

Again, when the propellant explorations put man on the edge of outer space, any further assault upward via jet propulsion was categorically ruled out by the inherent capabilities of space beyond the atmosphere. The particular capability, or the limitation imposed by it, is the fact that space has no air, or anything else for that matter, for propulsion. This meant then that for space exploration, the devices had to breathe their *own* air, so to speak. The answer here was rocketry in which provision is made for oxidizing its own fuel.

These three instances illustrate the opposition of propellant forces and inherent forces. The opposition sets certain limits; space as we know it appears to be the current envelope of the inherent capabilities, against which the forces of propellant explorations operate. For all we know, interplanetary travel, as well as intergalactic travel, may still be performed within the inherent capabilities already made known with regard to space. Maybe these capabilities are really more extensive than they are known to be today; we should recall that time was when man could not conceive of existence beyond the visible horizons.

Inherent capabilities are not a peculiar property of scientific knowledge and scientific parameters. Our statements relate to the "spin" of *ideational activity* itself. As such, it should be applicable equally well to all areas where ideational activity is involved. For instance, consider the national program to encourage additional childbirth in Nazi Germany. No matter how hard the propellant forces may explore the possibility of adding more members to the militia in the future, the inherent capabilities are constrained by the inevitable need for the period of gestation lasting approximately nine months. Further, no matter how intensely this effort proceeds, there are inevitable requirements of passage of time before babies who are born today will grow into adulthood.

Turning to another area, the aggregate sales revenue of the United States cannot exceed the *wealth* of the country. By wealth is meant not only the total value of products and services each year, but the sources from which stem the products and services. Thus, it is conceivable that the total sales revenue in the United States may exceed the total value of products and services in any year; which would indicate the borrowing across time and/or space: international borrowing or deficit financing. But sales revenue cannot exceed the wealth. Similarly, the profits of corporations can never exceed the sales revenues accruing to them. Propellant forces attempt to push the sales revenue to as high a limit as possible. Operating in the opposite direction are the inherent capabilities of the wealth of the United States, the "buffer distance" between the two, being available for open hunting, so to speak. The propellant explorations in behalf of extending profit try to lift it beyond its current percentage, closer to the sales revenue figures. But there is the inherent limitation on the expansion of profit percentages at 100 percent of sales revenue.

Consider an empirical instance. The propellant forces which create and promote new and different remedies to relieve headaches are bucking against the inherent limitation. This is imposed by the number of human beings, who by virtue of susceptibility to headaches, constitute the market for such remedies. With a population of 180,000,000 people, each one of whom — man, woman, child — getting one headache every day of the year, would create a market for 65,700,000,000 instances per year of demand for headache relief. Not all of the 180,000,000 will get a headache every day of the year; not all who get a headache every day, or any day, will seek relief from headache remedies. The inherent capability of the headache remedy market is thus in the neighborhood of 66,000,000,000 units per year given the population. The propellant forces of different headache-remedy manufacturers can push forward to capture as high a percentage of this relatively large figure of headache-remedy requirements as possible. But there does exist a "limit" imposed by the inherent capabilities of the market.

LINEAR EXTENSIONS AND QUANTUM JUMPS

The *spin* of the ideational activity is determined by inherent and propellant forces, and the *direction* of such spin is determined by the dimension of discovery chosen. What is a meaningful framework in which to view the orbital *paths* of such spins of ideational activity?

Ideational activity may profitably be considered to proceed along an orbit of extension and improvement of existing properties and performance of resources. Thus, the heating of milk in the tropics destroys the bacteria for a few hours, keeping the milk sterile. Additional heating could conceivably extend the sterilization effect by a few hours. Repeated heatings before the end of each sterilization period can conceivably keep the milk sterile for more hours, or even days.

While sterilization by heat was progressing in a linear fashion, the inherent capabilities of sterilization by heat must have come to the foreground. For instance, it was found virtually impossible to successfully kill off all the bacteria and their spores. The linear extension of the performance of maintaining the sterile state using heat suggested some form or other of continuous heating. The main objective was not, however, sterilization by heat as such, but preservation of food. Could the bacteria activity be curtailed, perhaps eliminated, without killing the bacteria themselves? Sterilization by refrigeration was the answer. However, the first major use of sterilization by refrigeration occurred accidentally.

> The first shipment of meat from Australia to Great Britain, about 1880, by refrigerated ship was not frozen before loading, nor was it intended that it be frozen. However it did freeze and the results led to freezing as a standard practice.[1]

Here was the quantum jump in the behavioral properties of the resources which led to the complete transformation of an entire organism, and opened up vistas undreamed of before.

MANIPULATIVE DEXTERITY

We posit that *manipulative dexterity* is the factor which permits the quantum jumps. Thus it is not enough if there occurs an accidental discovery of refrigeration as a means of preserving food; the process has to be reproducible under similar circumstances with similar effect. Further, the process should be improved and made safe for general use. Basically, what it involved would be summed up in the phrase manipulative dexterity, because what was achieved was neither the extension of the inherent capabilities, nor the successful propellant exploration. The latter would have merely meant indefinite application of heat in order to perpetuate the sterile state of food. The former would have meant the discovery of some sources other than bacteria which were really responsible for the decay and decomposition of food, leading to new avenues of scientific effort to preserve food. In this instance, bacteria still remained the identified cause of

---

[1] H. E. Cox and J. A. Tobey, "Food Preservation," *Encylopaedia Britannica* (Chicago: 1960), vol. 9, p. 456.

food spoilage; and the efficacy of heat as a means to provide sterile food was fast reaching its useful limit. The manipulative dexterity comprised of the discovery that bacteria were inactive in certain temperature ranges, and the technical ability to create and maintain such an environment of bacterial inactivity.

Similarly, we may look upon the ushering in of the space age. Way back in 1919 Robert H. Goddard, American rocket pioneer, had demonstrated the feasibility of rocket flights in which both the oxidizer and fuel were carried by the rocket itself. However, the means had to be found, some thirty years later, to overcome the gravitational and aerodynamic drag upon the satellite so that it could be shot into space by rocketry. In order to accomplish this, the satellite is thrust out far enough and fast enough, at about 18,000 miles an hour. This does not permit the satellite to escape completely from the earth's gravitational force and shoot off into outer space. The satellite trajectory is such that at this stage the vehicle should be acted on by the gravitational force of some other body, like the moon.

Here again, the manipulative dexterity comprised neither the extension of inherent capabilities, like the establishment of a new escape velocity, below 25,000 miles per hour, nor an advance in propellant exploration, like the direct acceleration through 25,000 plus miles per hour. Manipulative dexterity comprised a means by which the aerodynamic drag and the gravitational drag were overcome not simultaneoulsy but at different times, using the period to manipulate the trajectory of the vehicle without letting it fly out into outer space nor fall to the ground.

Admittedly, the orbital progress of ideational activity would very much depend upon the dimension of discovery and the rate of advancement of the propellant forces. This is what accounts for the different rates of progress from sterilization by heat to sterilization by refrigeration, and from atmospheric flights to space flights. We indicate this fact in Figure 7 by means of the different types of orbits that are pursued by the different types of ideational activity. Even as the orbital paths, so also the quantum jumps bear the imprint of the particular dimension of discovery and the progress of propellant explorations.

LOCUS OF REALIZATION

The discoveries, whether furthering the understanding in the dimension of size, speed, length, temperature, or any other dimension, all revolve around the axis of discovery identified by $E = mc^2$. Different types of matter, and different types of energy, are generated and put to use at different times for different purposes. Nevertheless, the basic underlying

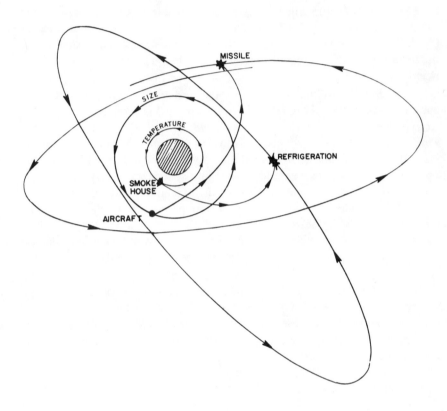

Figure 7. TRANSFORMATION OF ORGANISMS BASED ON QUANTUM JUMPS IN BEHAVIORAL
PROPERTIES OF RESOURCES.

factor is that they all share the parentage of the equality of matter with
energy.

We may view the matter-energy equation to be a general statement,
of which special formulations are made and remade in different dimensions
and at different times. We represent this in Figure 8 by characterizing the
axis of discovery by the Einstein equation $E = mc^2$. The spinning sphere of
ideational activity, traveling along the orbits of discovery and guided by the
dimension of discovery, traces out a *locus of realization*. As seen in Figure
8, the contributions to the locus by the different dimensions are substantially different from each other. However, they share in common the feature
of realization of the great generalization contained in the Einstein equation.

Thus we have the spinning spheres of ideational activity, which are
operated on by opposing forces of inherent capabilities and propellant

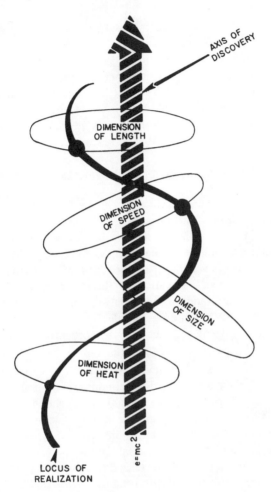

Figure 8. AXIS OF DISCOVERY AND LOCUS OF REALIZATION.

explorations. Spin takes place along an orbit of discovery of the behavorial properties of resources and organisms. The changes in behavioral properties of the resources take place in discontinuous, quantum jumps. Manipulative dexterity mediates the change from a mere linear extension of behavioral properties to a new level of behavioral properties, which, in turn, proceeds in a different orbit of its own. These quantum jumps result in successive realizations of the great generalization expressed in E $= mc^2$.

Thus there is room for a wide range of spins of ideational activity, including absence of any propellant exploration. The direction of the spin is determined by the dimension of discovery, which choice itself may be overlapping and ambivalent. To that extent, the resulting orbital paths of the spinning spheres of ideational activity will also be crisscrossing and zigzagging. Concurrently, and independently of the orbital paths of ideational activity, elements of manipulative dexterity can be gathering forces of their own. It is likely that the expanding control of man's enviornment will be conditioned much more by the judicious choices of the dimensions of discovery and application of propellant forces, and limited much less by the inherent capabilities of resources.

ACTUALIZATION OF IDEAS AND DECISIVENESS OF DECISIONS: INTERNAL GREENLIGHT

The path from idea to output is seldom short or direct. No matter how brilliant the discoveries made by the research personnel, and how perceptive and profound the profile of things-to-come envisaged by the long-range planners, the conversion of an idea into an output will be very much subject to the tempo of innovation of the organism itself, whether it be ultraconservative, ultramodern, or in-between in terms of its preparedness to host new ideas. While the irresistible innovation meets sometimes the immovable development policies of the organism, time marches on, instructing the wise and dragging the fool.

Long-range, objective, evaluations of the capabilities of organism(s) can take their cue from the technometric structure of the material resources at the disposal of the organism. Technometric structure, we pointed out, should disclose certain input-output relationships (page 55). Whether the output of the organism involves a system of international inspection via space platforms or the sale of chewing gum via drugstores, or hundreds of chemical products which enter into scores of other products, *the nature of the output should be established in its relationship with the corresponding input.* The technometric structure of these output-input relationships over time of the particular organism must aim at disclosing two types of information: (1) the peculiarities and the specialities of the primary resources that are used, and (2) inherent sequencing involved in the translation of an idea into an output. The behavioral properties and structural propensities of the primary resources were discussed earlier; they are the subject matter of the first type of information.

The "blue-sky thinking" about desirable outputs of the organism in the long run will necessarily be based on what is currently known of the technometric structure of the resources themselves. In order to bring these ideas to fruition, however, *technical support* is essential: technical support for the engineering realization of the capabilities inherent in the technometric structure. In other words, it is not enough if it is conceptually possible that a solid propellant can be manufactured instead of a liquid propellant; there should also be the technological capability to generate the energy from the solid efficiently. It was known for a long time that matter contained energy; and from 1905, when Einstein's famous $E = mc^2$ equation was available, that matter *was* energy. But it was not until 1945 that the energy property of matter was spectacularly demonstrated over Hiroshima. As we have seen, Robert H. Goddard showed that the rocket could breathe in space because it carried its own air with it, so to speak; that is, it contains both fuel and oxidizer. Goddard demonstrated this fact *experimentally* as early as 1919 but it was not until the late 1950's that the means was found for the rocket to overcome the very considerable force of gravity, enabling it to pierce the atmospheric envelope and get into outer space. The upshot of these empirical situations is that adequate consideration must be given to the technical support that is required to translate the idea into an output.

This assessment of the present capabilities of the organism with respect to the changing profile of the industry of which it is a component is not a mere state of mind. Demands of transformation consequent on the quantum jumps in the behavioral properties of the resources currently or potentially available to the organism should be met squarely ahead of time. It is the *preparedness to make the necessary changes to meet the chances* that marks the difference between the successful survival, and the scrambling for existence.

> General Dynamics is the nation's largest defense contractor, its sales last year [1961] [were] more than $2,000,000,000. Largely as a result of the phase-out of the B-58 the company expects sales to be 10% lower this year [1962] than last.
>
> But General Dynamics has diversified widely among commercial operations, such as building materials and telecommunications, advanced research and defense production. Its defense work ranges from making the submarines that carry the Polaris missile to producing the Atlas intercontinental ballistic missile . . . .
>
> The diversification policy of General Dynamics stood the company in good stead in its effort to enter the commercial jet transportation market.
>
> That effort by the Convair division cost the company $425,000,000. If Convair had been alone on that venture, some believe it would have gone under. Diversification, aside from shoring up the company for changing defense needs, also came in handy in more prosaic civilian activities.[2]

2 John M. Lee, "Pentagon Moves Cause Woes for Two Big Aircraft Companies," *New York Times,* Apr. 29, 1962, p. 14.

The death of an idea can take place in any of the many steps involved in the inherent sequencing from idea to output. At least three major inevitable phases may be visualized in the progress from an idea to an output. They are: (1) Idea to go-no-go decision regarding development of the output, (2)From development to go-no-go decision on production of prototype of output, and (3) From prototype production to go-no-go decision on production of output.

PHASE I: IDEA TO DEVELOPMENT

A schematic presentation is attempted in Figures 9–13 to highlight the many steps that are involved in each of these three major decision phases. Any effort to structure the requirements in terms of time units would be extremely hazardous, because of the wide range of requirements and capabilities that are available in each developmental area. Therefore, reference is made to the succession in time by merely referring to them as t_i $(i = 1 - n)$.

Thus the idea is indicated as developing in time t_1 (Figure 9). It may originate with the engineer; with the customer; with the liaison engineer who mediates between the organism and the customer; with the operations researcher, who has access to an overview of the different activities of the organism; with the management which does have the overview of the various activities of the organism; or with some other source. These different strands of thought, even if they were to occur simultaneously, would still have to be funneled through the liaison engineer who has to take it up with the customer, except in the instance where the idea originates with the customer himself. As a result of this liaison that may be performed with either the present customers or potential customers, there is bound to be some modification of the idea itself by means of cross-fertilization of the points of view of the organism and the customer. The first formal report on these excursions would be in the form of a technical report, which is indicated to take place at time t_5.

The generation of the idea is allocated one *unit of time*. Its processing by the liaison engineer, another unit. The liaison function involving the potential customer is allotted another unit; so also the modification of the idea by the liaison engineer and the potential customer. The technical report is supposed to be made in two units of time. These time-unit allocations are admittedly gross oversimplifications. However, *relative lengths* of these periods, viz., the allocation of twice the time for writing the technical report as that for the first processing of the idea, may not altogether be unreasonable.

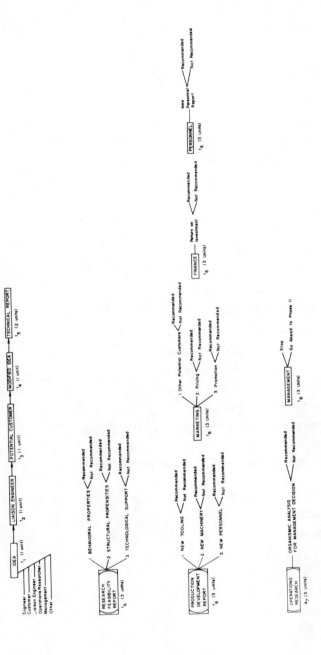

Figure 9. INHERENT SEQUENCING: IDEA TO OUTPUT—PHASE I: IDEA TO DEVELOPMENT.

UNIT

Phase I: Idea to Development: IRD

1. Idea	6
2. Recommendations—Components	18
Recommendations—OR	
3. Decision—Management:	
Go-No Go on Development	3

Phase II: Development to Prototype: DPPPSSSSD

4. Development	10
5. Production	10
6. Promotion and Promise	4
7. Preparation to Ship Samples	2
8. Sample Shipment	2
9. Sample Receipt by Customer	3
10. Sample Feedback by Customer	2
11. Sales	2
12. Decision—Management:	
Go-No Go on Production of Prototype	3

Phase III: Prototype to Final Output: PPPPPSD

13. Prototype Production	15
14. Promotion	5
15. Preparation	3
16. Prototype Shipment	3
17. Prototype Customer Receipt	2
18. Prototype Customer Feedback	3
19. Sales Order	3
20. Decision	4

Figure 10. IDEA TO OUTPUT: INHERENT SEQUENCING — IRD; DPPPSSSSD; PPPPPSD.

From the idea stage we proceed to the recommendation stage. Recommendations have to be made by all the constituent components of the organism which would be affected by the success or otherwise of the idea. The research component of the organism should definitely be responsible for preparing a feasibility report which will comprise the technometric structure as well as the technical support that would be required in the prosecution of the idea, transforming it from an idea into an output. The production operations would have to conceive of the new tooling, the new machinery, and the new personnel or new skills for existing personnel that would be required in order to bring off the idea. The marketing component of the organism would be concerned with other potential customers to whom the output may be sold; the pricing of the product now and in the future; and the promotional efforts that are required to bring before the potential public the necessary knowledge about the existence and capabilities of the proposed product. The finance component of the organism would be responsible for preparing for management a return on investment. The personnel component of the organism would be concerned with the impact of the prosecution on personnel deployment. The recommendations by the operations research group would presumably be from the organismic point of view, instead of the atomistic point of view associated with the major components of the organism: production, marketing, finance, personnel, research. Recommendation stage is allotted as much as 18 units of time, composed of 3 units each for each of the 6 major components of the organism involved in making recommendations about the prosecution of the idea. The preparation of feasibility reports by the research component is accorded 150 percent of the time that is allotted the liaison engineer to make the technical report, assuming the relative duration of time required for making definitive proposals by the components of the organism to be 150 percent of that for the presentation of the idea itself by the liaison function.

The first terminal decision by top management would be a go-no-go decision on development efforts for the output as proposed by the idea. This process is allotted as much time as it takes each of the major components of the organism to make the recommendations. Even at this rapid pace of accomplishments in the idea, recommendations, and decision stages comprising the first phase of translating the idea into an output, a total of 27 time units is found to be the minimum necessary. If the unit of time is the month, two years and three months shall have gone by before the decision is made as to whether or not to go ahead with the development of the output as represented in the idea.

We see in Figure 11 a Case Study in the translation of an idea into

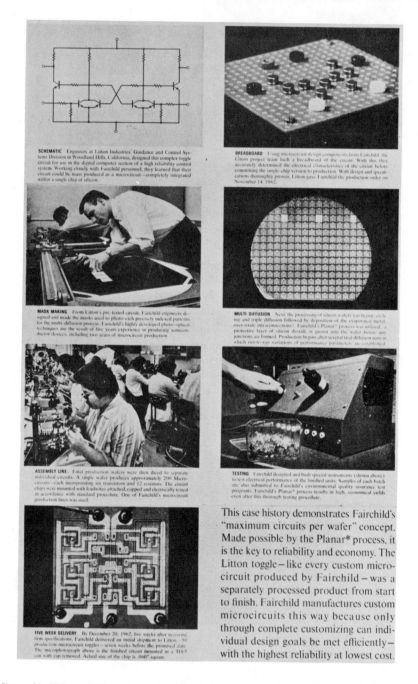

SCHEMATIC Engineers at Litton Industries' Guidance and Control Systems Division in Woodland Hills, California, designed this complex toggle circuit for use in the digital computer section of a high reliability control system. Working closely with Fairchild personnel, they learned that their circuit could be mass produced as a microcircuit—completely integrated within a single chip of silicon.

BREADBOARD Using microcircuit design components from Fairchild, the Litton project team built a breadboard of the circuit. With this they accurately determined the electrical characteristics of the circuit before committing the single-chip version to production. With design and specifications thoroughly proven, Litton gave Fairchild the production order on November 14, 1962.

MASK MAKING From Litton's pre-tested circuit, Fairchild engineers designed and made the masks used to photo-etch precisely indexed patterns for the multi-diffusion process. Fairchild's highly developed photo-optical techniques are the result of five years experience in producing semiconductor devices, including two years of microcircuit production.

MULTI-DIFFUSION Next, the processing of silicon wafers was begun: etching and triple diffusion followed by deposition of the evaporated metal over-mode intraconnections. Fairchild's Planar* process was utilized: a protective layer of silicon dioxide is grown into the wafer before any junctions are formed. Production begins after several trial diffusion runs on which run-to-run variations of performance parameters are established.

ASSEMBLY LINE Final production wafers were then diced to separate individual circuits. A single wafer produces approximately 200 Microcircuits—each incorporating six transistors and 12 resistors. The circuit chips were mounted with leadwires attached, capped and electrically tested in accordance with standard procedure. One of Fairchild's microcircuit production lines was used.

TESTING Fairchild designed and built special instruments (shown above) to test electrical performance of the finished units. Samples of each batch are also submitted to Fairchild's environmental quality assurance test programs. Fairchild's Planar* process results in high, economical yields even after this thorough testing procedure.

FIVE WEEK DELIVERY By December 20, 1962, five weeks after receiving firm specifications, Fairchild delivered an initial shipment to Litton - 50 production microcircuit toggles—seven weeks before the promised date. The microphotograph above is the finished circuit mounted in a TO-5 can with cap removed. Actual size of the chip is .060" square.

This case history demonstrates Fairchild's "maximum circuits per wafer" concept. Made possible by the Planar* process, it is the key to reliability and economy. The Litton toggle—like every custom microcircuit produced by Fairchild—was a separately processed product from start to finish. Fairchild manufactures custom microcircuits this way because only through complete customizing can individual design goals be met efficiently—with the highest reliability at lowest cost.

Figure 11. FROM SCHEMATIC TO FAIRCHILD PRODUCTION MICROCIRCUIT...IN 5 WEEKS

an output as reported by Fairchild. In Table VIII the parallel steps are identified so that the time dimension can be evaluated. For instance, the schematic in the Case Study corresponds to both the customer idea and Liaison Engineer idea in Figure 9, requiring 1 time unit each. Similarly, the mask making in the Case Study corresponds to the feasibility report by research in Figure 9, and so on. The five-week period (25 days) in the Case Study corresponds to 21 time units in Figures 10 and 12. In this case, 1 time unit = 1.2 days.

In Figure 11, we have an actual case study basically reflecting Phase I and Phase II sequences. In the context of intense competition for new ideas and new outputs, it is quite likely that the unit of time may not be the month. Whether or not the unit is the month is not the question; but the inevitable fact is that there have to elapse certain blocks of time before even the first phase of the translation of the idea into an output can take place.

PHASE II: DEVELOPMENT TO PROTOTYPE

In the second Phase of the decision process (Figure 12), the progress is from the development of the output to the go-no-go decision on the production of the prototype. In this stage the output is no longer a

TABLE VIII

CORRESPONDING TIME UNITS IN CASE STUDY AND PHASES I, II

CASE STUDY (Fig. 11)	TIME UNITS	PHASE (Figs. 10, 12)	AND	TIME UNITS
Schematic	2.3 days	I	Customer Idea	1
Breadboard design		I	Liaison Engineer Idea	1
Mask-making	3.5 days	I	Research; Feasibility Report	3
Multidiffusion	12.0 days	II	Production	10
Assembly line				
Testing	1.2 days	II	Preshipment Tests	1
Delivery	6.0 days	II	Shipment	2
		II	Customer Receives shipment	3
Total	5 weeks (25 days)		Total	21

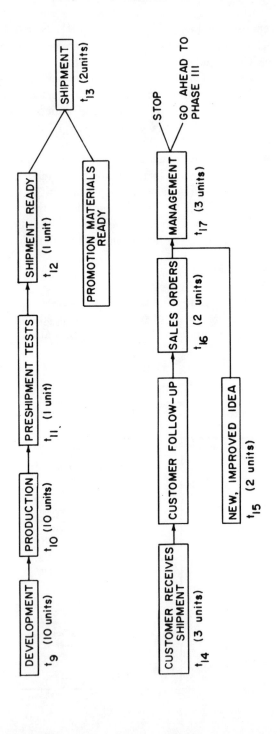

Figure 12. INHERENT SEQUENCING: IDEA TO OUTPUT — PHASE II: DEVELOPMENT TO PROTOTYPE.

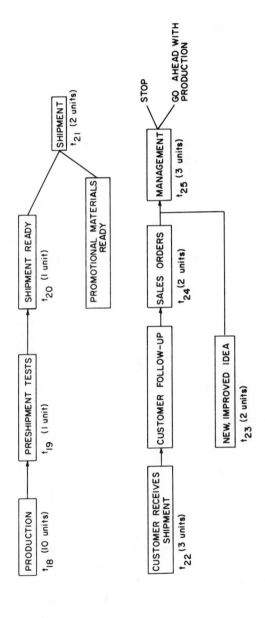

Figure 13. INHERENT SEQUENCING: IDEA TO OUTPUT — PHASE III: PROTOTYPE TO OUTPUT.

"research" product or a laboratory product. It has been established that the product can be made at least on a small scale, beyond the dimension of the laboratory production for research purposes. The original proposals of the production component of the organism will be put to test in the course of actual attempts at manufacture of the output on a sufficiently large scale to permit shipment of samples to customers for the particular output. Now that the development and production efforts have translated the abstract idea into reality, this fact needs to be proclaimed persuasively to a wide range of customers — both present and potential. There will essentially be promises involved at this stage, the output itself being as yet hardly born. Once the production of the samples is over, preshipment tests and other efforts to minimize the deficiencies in performance of this altogether new output should be undertaken. Following such preparations, the sample shipment takes place, which is duly received by the customer. An important step follows: the customer feedback on the performance of the sample by the customer. If the customer is pleased, he may place a sufficiently attractive size of order(s) for additional samples of the prototype. It is almost certain that in this case the customer would also inject additional requirements and/or specifications of his own for the performance of the output. The proof of the pudding is in the eating; the proof of the idea is in the acceptance, evidenced by the size of the order for further supplies of the output. This sets the stage for the second major decision by management of a go-no-go nature on the production of the prototype of the output. Even at this stage, it is likely that the decision would be to produce a larger quantity than the original sample, but not quite to go all the way with the tooling-up for production on a large scale.

PHASE III: PROTOTYPE TO OUTPUT

The third Phase of management decision (Figure 13) follows a series of steps essentially similar to the second Phase — with the major exception that there would be no requirement for development efforts as in the second Phase. Other improvements, of course, could be made in this Phase, but they are not absolutely essential. Development was allotted 10 units in Phase II, which is not required in Phase III. However, larger production runs and shipment lots in Phase III use up additional units of time for production and shipment functions than in Phase II, leaving the total units of effort unchanged at 38 units.

This does not mean that the respective time units have to be sequenced from one end to the other. For instance, the promotion and promise in both Phases II and III can proceed concurrently with the production operation. The customer feedbacks on the sample and on the prototype can also be carried on along with the writing of sales orders for additional shipment.

At the same time, there are rigidities in the sequencing of the steps from idea to output. One cannot ship samples of prototypes before they are manufactured. The customer cannot provide feedback on the outputs until after he receives them. There are minimal times required for translocation of the samples and the outputs, whether it be by mail, by carrier, by public or private transportation.

In order to be effective, management decision-making has to await customer feedback, in the form of qualitative reactions, as well as in the form of quantitative measure of endorsement represented by the size of sales orders. Management decision-making may be visualized as a *sequential* process, a sequence of decision being made at the end of Phase I, to be reviewed at least further at the end of Phase II and Phase III. The decision may be made that: (1) Development of the output shall proceed; (2) Should the development be reasonably successful, then the samples shall be submitted for customer inspection and approval; (3) Should there be a reasonable response from the customers, a prototype of the output shall be manufactured; (4) The prototype shall be submitted for customer inspection and approval; (5) If there is a reasonable response for the prototypes, the terminal decision will be made to proceed with the production of output on a commercial scale. In other words, in Phase I the decision is more than an experimental one; it becomes a tentative plan to proceed with the entire spectrum of steps involved in the translation of the idea into an output. Within the framework of such a step-by-step procedure, the management go-no-go decision-making in Phases II and III would be adapted to an intelligent learning from the performance vis-à-vis promises of the output up to that period.

INNOVATING EFFECTIVENESS

Continuing extension of conceptual breakthroughs beyond current resource capabilities is pursued via dimensions of discovery. To translate the ideas so generated, technical support is indispensable.

Even when technical support favors the translation of the idea to output, there has to be faced the inevitable, inherent sequencing of such a translation. The critical role of the three major management decision-making discussed in the preceding section constitutes the bulwark of the sequencing process. Since whether the ideas blossom or perish depends on these decision processes, they bear closer scrutiny.

By innovating effectiveness we mean: (1) *How effectively is the profile of innovation drawn up?, and* (2) *How effectively does the profile of innovation "get through" to the management decision-making?*

In order to effectively draw the profile of innovation which ought to be entered into by the organism, commensurate with the capabilities of its resources and the dimensions of discovery, the germ of the idea has to be properly planted, watered, and nourished before germination. What is the nature of the real world that lends credence to the profile of innovation as a potentially acceptable method of procedure? When Edward Teller proposed that smaller and lighter warheads should be available on a time scale compatible with submarine development, this profile of innovation was not acceptable until he could produce historical evidence of the trends in warhead dimensions which was convincing enough to set the pace of design for what became the *Polaris*.

In other words, whether an extension of the behavioral properties of the resources is involved or a quantum jump in their behavioral properties, cause has to be shown why such extensions or jumps are consistent with the known dimensions and propensities of the real world. This necessarily involves a certain amount of projecting the past into the future — a projection which may be rejected as inadequate, or used as a springborad to suggest linear extensions or quantum jumps. All history is biased history. The bias is injected by the compiler of historic events simply because of his own vantage point. His biased collection can be made to construe a structure. Such a structure can be used to assess the probable developments in the future. A prediction of the future as a mere replica of the past does have the appeal of simplicity, although it may be unsatisfactory.

The effectiveness of the profile of innovations that is drawn may be gauged in terms of the method of employment of the past to yield a structure which in turn is utilized to generate a possible development in the future. We can divide the profile construction efforts in terms of their relative sophistication. Needless to say, sophistication is no guarantee of either validity or reliability. Should the methods employed be appropriate to the particular set of past information, then the more sophisticated the method of profile construction the more likely it is to obtain as adequate an extension of the past into the future as is technically feasible.

Management Activity Horizon and Degree of Data-Processing Sophistication

In Table IX we identify the different levels of sophistication employed in constructing the profile of the future on the basis of the past, corresponding to different management acitivity horizons. *Management activity horizon* is a classification based on the answer to the question: How far from here-and-now to the hereafter? This horizon is divided into five: immediate, at the one end, and infinite at the other, with three divisions of finite horizon in between.

TABLE IX

CLASSIFICATION OF INNOVATION PROFILE CONSTRUCTION EFFORTS

DEGREE OF DATA PROCESSING SOPHISTICATION ↓ / MANAGEMENT ACTIVITY HORIZON →	IMMEDIATE	FINITE I	FINITE II	FINITE III	INFINITE
A. TOTAL SERIES					
1. Seat-of-the-pants	11	12	13	14	15
2. Nonlinear growth models	21	22	23	24	25
B. COMPONENT SERIES					
3. Trend	31	32	33	34	35
4. Cyclical	41	42	43	44	45
5. Seasonal	51	52	53	54	55
6. Combinations of (3, 4, 5)	61	62	63	64	65
C. COMPLEX MEASURES					
7. Linear programming	71	72	73	74	75
8. Dynamic programming	81	82	83	84	85
9. Simulation of management activity	91	92	93	94	95

The data-processing sophistication involved in the profile construction efforts is divided into three levels. At the low end of the scale, one encounters perhaps the most popular of all data processing methods: seat-of-the-pants method. At the other end of the scale, one could visualize a full-blown simulation of management activity. If the latter were to have any advantage over the former, it would be due particularly to the realistic representation of the intuitive forces that are imbedded in the oft-practiced and little-understood process of selection of variables, and of the influences on the variables which are most relevant to the shaping of the future. The approach of dynamic programming is given the highest degree of data-processing sophistication, next only to simulation. This is because dynamic programming is generally applied to *segments* of management activity, whereas the simulation of management activity applies to management as a whole. The provision of progressive learning, or adaptive process of learning sequentially, available in dynamic programming, is not obtained in the technique of linear programming. Therefore, linear programming is given the highest rank next to dynamic programming in terms of the degree of data-processing sophistication.

Going back to the other end of the scale, which begins with seat-of-the-pants method, nonlinear growth models are listed as higher in data processing sophistication. This is a generic term, covering orthogonal polynomials; exponential smoothing; and logistic, Gompertz, and other growth curves.

Simulation of management activity for one, and the seat-of-the-pants estimates, for another, are directed towards total time series in that they deal with facts and figures of past experience as a whole; and may be looked upon as profile construction efforts based on the *overall* information. Contrasted with this are the component series analysis, particularly trend analysis, cyclical analysis, seasonal analysis, and appropriate combinations of these three. It also includes other types of time series analysis, in which not the traditional T, S, and C components, but the irregular component I is highlighted.

Thus the classification of innovation profile construction efforts may be identified in terms of the corresponding rows and columns. Seat-of-the-pants applied to the immediate activity horizon would be row 1 and column 1; hence indicated as 11. Seat-of-the-pants method applied to the infinite horizon of management would be 15; the same method applied to activity horizons — Finite I would be 12; Finite II, 13; and Finite III, 14. Simulation of management activity is accorded the highest degree of sophistication in the data-processing scale. Therefore the simulation of management activity applied to the immediate horizon is referred to as 91, to the infinite horizon, 95. Similarly, dynamic programming applied to the immediate management activity horizon would be 81, to the infinite would be 85; the three finite periods being given numbers 82, 83, and 84. Seasonal analysis supplied to management applied to immediate horizon of management activity would be 51; to Finite I horizon would be 52; Finite II, 53; Finite III, 54; and the infinite, 55: and so on.

Profile Construction Presentation and Intervening Doors

Crucial to the effectiveness of profile construction efforts is the requirement that the decision-maker at the respective management level must be accessible to the profile constructor(s). A crude, but graphic, way of indicating accessibility would be the number of doors the profile constructor has to pass through before reaching the authority who can sanction the implementation of the implications of the profiles constructed.

In an informal survey* of the classification of innovation profile construction efforts where the contents of Table IX were employed, the near-universality of the seat-of-the-pants method of estimation of the future on the basis of the past was striking. So also was the scant attention paid to the infinite horizons, or even the distant finite horizons, the preoccupation being generally on the immediate. This was revealing, considering the fact that the participants in the survey themselves were personnel reportedly charged with the function of profile construction.

Turning to the number of doors between profile constructors and the authority for implementation, the largest number of doors separated the profile-construction efforts of the highest degree of sophistication from the appropriate management levels, while the fewer number of doors stood between the seat-of-the-pants and nonlinear growth model efforts to construct profiles, and managements.

Admittedly, no definitive conclusions can be drawn from such a small sample as was available, for which reason only the *qualitative* highlights are presented here. A tenuous observation, perhaps not altogether invalid, may be made about the predominant shying away from venturing into the management activity horizons beyond the immediate and the present, and the relative inaccessibility of management to the profile constructors employing data-processing methods of increased sophistication. Can it, for instance, be suggested that the management generally tends to keep its nose to the ground, preoccupied with the present to the exclusion of the future? Perhaps the models of profile construction employing more sophisticated methods of data processing are not sufficiently down-to-earth to suit the taste of many in management. Nevertheless, it should be admitted that when the degree of relevance approximates the degree of elegance, the more powerful the method the more likely is its usefulness as a guide to disclose the strengths and weaknesses inherent in the available information. Can it then be a general distrust of the mathematical and the machine-oriented that encourages management to build a large number of intermediary doors between the more elegant construction efforts and themselves?

The preoccupation with the present, and the avoidance of the sophisticated, are not features peculiar to any particular size of company: in the survey were included companies employing from 1,500 to 120,000.

* Conducted at the American Management Association Clinic on Data Processing for Business Planning, New York City, March 1962.

While the object of the survey was not to arrive at a quantative analysis of the effectiveness of profile construction and its acceptance, the survey did take place at the end of three days of intensive discussion centered around the general topic of profile construction. In other words, the data that were presented were provided by people who were motivated at a level above the ordinary and they were conscientiously cognizant of the implications of the issues involved.

The purpose of this section has been to highlight the many slips between the cup and the lip; between the profile construction and the implementation of its implications. The number of doors considered was indicative of upward inaccessibility between the profile constructor and the management decision-maker. Corresponding to this *vertical* communication barrier, there are also *horizontal* communication barriers imposed on the profile-construction effort by apathy, ignorance, and downright antipathy of components of the organism generating pieces of information, which by themselves are only information, but which in appropriate combination can yield intelligence for the organism.

PART III

PROCESSING OF INFORMATION

The past observe, what is to come foresee,
Like Janus, facing both ways equally.

CATO, *Disticha, ii, 27*

All these tidal gatherings, growth and decay,
Shining and darkening, are forever
Renewed; and the whole cycle impenitently
Resolves, and all the past is future: —
Make it a difficult world . . . . for practical people.

ROBINSON JEFFERS, *Practical People*

CHAPTER FIVE

PROCESSING CURRENT INFORMATION TO PREDICT POTENTIAL PRODUCTS

Getting down to cases, as it were, from the discussion of the external factors of technological feasibility and axis of discovery, on the one hand, and the internal factors of long-range planning and organismic decision-making, on the other, we ask the question: How can the organism process present information to predict potential products?

Even as the periodic table indicated, by its very structure, missing elements, so also Periodic Table of Product Diversification (PTPD) is proposed as a systematic means for a continuing review of an organism's output portfolio.

One feature of such portfolio review is that it provides for explicit recognition of both the producer's and consumer's objectives. An output is intended to satisfy at least one want, and its ability to satisfy the want, to be called its *S-Index,* is evaluated by the consumer in terms of the vital nature of the want satisfied, to be called its *V-Index.*

One thing is certain of every output: it is born, it grows, it matures, it declines, it dies. The contribution of each product to a particular organism also rises from nothing, to something — possibly something highly significant — and after it reaches its peak contribution fades into lesser degree of significance, finally vanishing into virtually nothing. These processes of "growth and decay are forever renewed"; and in the sense, "the whole cycle impenitently resolves." Therefore, it behooves the organism to be aware of the life cycle of contribution of its many outputs so that the high noon of contribution by a particular product or group of products may not lull it into a sense of false security. On the other hand, knowing that high noon yields place to evening, the Janus of organismic management should view "both ways equally," and wisely provide for the introduction of another product or group of products to take the place of the current leader.

PRODUCT LIFE CYCLE

The life cycle of any product is represented in Figure 14. The stages of growth are called G_0 (Conception), G_1 (Infancy), G_2 (Rapid Growth), G_3 (Maturation), and G_4 (Decline and Death).

In instances where a large number of products are involved, and where varying degrees of information are available about the respective

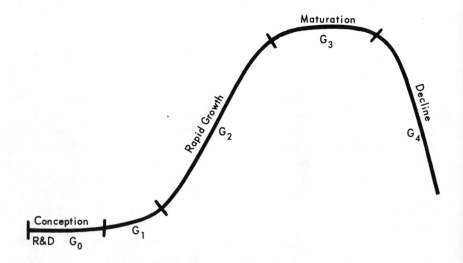

Figure 14. PRODUCT LIFE CYCLE.

performances of the products, the *new* pieces of information are likely to be of varying significance. Thus, for a relatively new product, additions to its history are much more significant than an older product. Again, information indicating turning points in the life cycle of either old or new products are more important than that indicating a continuance of the life-cycle stage.

What we need is a rapid, repeatable, means of handling new information about every single product in a manner fitting the respective importance of the information to the existing history. This calls for a differentiated method of treating new pieces of data.

As new information is added, new insights should also be obtainable about the performance of the product. Two types of new insights may be visualized: one, relating to the stage of growth of the product; two, relating to the new forecast of the performance of the product.

EXPONENTIAL SMOOTHING

R. G. Brown's exponential smoothing can be adapted to meet these requirements.

> Exponential smoothing is a special kind of moving average that does not require keeping a long historical record in the active file and thus cuts down on the data-processing time required. Like other moving averages, it has a stable response to changes, but the rate of response can be adjusted readily.... To get a new estimate of the average demand, add to the previous estimate a fraction of the amount by which demand this month exceeds that estimate. Note that under this rule, demand below the estimate is the same as saying it exceeded the estimate by a negative quantity, and adding a fraction of a negative quantity would decrease the estimate.
>
> The fraction used is a "smoothing constant," and is conventionally represented by α, the Greek letter alpha. We could abbreviate our rule in the form of an equation:
>
> New estimate $=$ old estimate $+ \alpha$ (new demand — old estimate)
> Or by rearranging the terms a little:
>
> New estimate $= \alpha$ (new demand) $+ (1 - \alpha)$ (old estimate) . . .
>
> Since we know that the average computed by exponential smoothing will lag behind demand with a systematic trend, if we could estimate the magnitude of the trend, we could make the necessary correction to eliminate the lag. . . .
>
> We know that the increase in the estimated average in successive months will equal the increase in the actual demand. Therefore, we could take as an estimate of the current trend the difference

Current trend = new average — old average

Random fluctuations in the demand will cause minor fluctuations in the estimated average demand and hence in the current trend. We have, however, ready to hand, a means for estimating the average of a fluctuating quantity. The average trend could then be computed by

New trend = α (current trend) $+$ $(1 - \alpha)$ (old trend)

I have shown elsewhere[1] that this method of computing the trend is in fact the least-squares estimate of the trend, if the weights given to the demand in each previous month are the same as those used in computing the average.

The correction for the lag due to trend can then be expressed as

$$\text{Expected demand} = \text{new average} + \frac{(1 - \alpha)}{\alpha} (\text{new trend})$$

In this form, it is necessary only to store the previously calculated values for the average and for the trend, so that the data processing is still simple.[2]

A particular smoothing constant, α, determines the weight given to the past information in arriving at the new estimate. Viewed from the life-cycle point of view, products in the different stages of growth will necessarily provide information of varying importance. Thus, when a product is in the maturation stage, information in the immediately preceding time period will be more important than the information relating to the early years of its origin. Appropriate value of α, which closely approximates the given instances of data, can be arrived at *empirically*. The most suitable value of α will be that value which provides the closest predictions.

It must be emphasized here that whatever may be the attractiveness of a measure which minimizes the deviations of the observed values from the expected values for the entire series of observations, this may not necessarily be attractive to the line management. The particular product manager is interested most keenly in as close a prediction for *his own product* in the past years on the basis of a particular α so that he could, with some confidence, employ the same value of α to predict the immediate future sales of his product. To him, it is of little consequence if there were

---

[1] R.G. Brown, "Exponential Smoothing for Predicting Demand," Tenth National Meeting of Operations Research Society of America, San Francisco, November 16, 1956.

[2] R.G. Brown, *Statistical Forecasting for Inventory Control* (New York; McGraw-Hill Book Company, Inc., 1959), pp. 45-46; 48-50.

an α which minimized the total deviations between the observed and expected values for *all the products* of the company. His interest is in being convinced that a particular value of α is most meaningful in maintaining a reasonable closeness between the predicted values and the actual values during the years for which data are available, so that he can place a reasonable degree of confidence in the pediction about the next time period.

Goodness of Fit

A statistical measure which evaluates the deviation of the observed from the expected value is chi square (χ^2). In order to determine how "good" the fit is, the relationship between the "expected" frequencies on the basis of the fitted curve and the "observed" frequencies must be studied. The ideal situation would be when both coincide. In that case, "observed-expected" would be 0. The mere algebraic difference between the observed and expected occurences by itself does not indicate clearly that the fit is worse at one point where the algebraic value is higher than at another data point corresponding to which the algebraic value is lower. It stands to reason that the correspondence between expected and observed should be measured against the expected. Squaring the "observed-expected," and dividing by the "expected," we find the measure of divergence between the observed and expected for each data point; and adding the individual divergences we compute χ^2 for the set of observations. How significant are the divergences? We compare the computed χ^2 value with the appropriate χ^2 table value. The chi-square (χ^2) table indicates the probability of *exceeding* the table value for any given degrees of freedom by chance.

Provision should be made in the computer program to measure the "goodness of fit" provided by the different values of χ^2. The first χ^2 calculation would be corresponding to the nth data point, where we predict the nth data point on the basis of the $(n - 1)$ points, the $(n + 1)$th data point on the basis of the first n, and so on. The divergence of the observed value from the predicted value is measured for each of the data points. These individual divergences are divided by the respective "expected" values and summed to derive a χ^2 value.

(1) The χ^2 value obtained on the basis of the predictions can be compared at *any stage* with the corresponding theoretical value of χ^2. (2) This can be done for the *different degrees of confidence,* depending on the degree of risk that the industrial product manager is willing to undertake. (3) This procedure also provides for the *pinpointing of extremely large variations* which would vitiate any computation of the value for the entire instances of

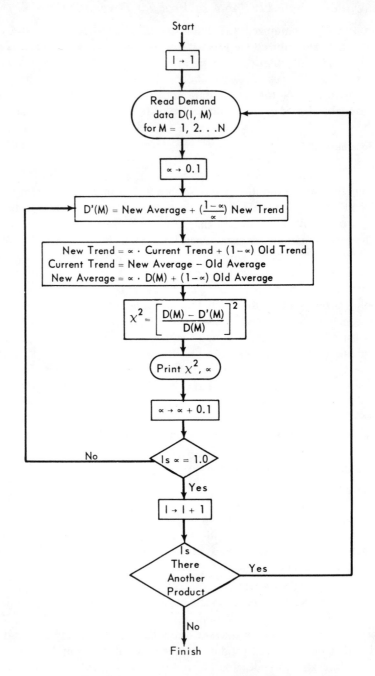

Figure 15. FLOW-CHART FOR EXPONENTIAL SMOOTHING PROGRAM.

data. Should there be any such violent divergences, they should be removed from contributing to the χ^2 for the entire set of observations. However it is quite possible that a particular value of α may be most appropriate to describe the sales of products up to the certain data point where the divergence occurs, even when the divergence is far too much for χ^2 to be meaningful for the *entire span* of data points.

Since the criterion of choice of α-value is the minimization of the divergence between the observed and expected values of the demand data, $D(M)$, for $M = 1,2 \ldots N$, the computer program can be instructed to compare successive values of χ^2 for the particular variable.

Figure 15 shows the flow chart for the computer program.

COMPUTERIZED IDENTIFICATION OF STAGES-OF-GROWTH

In exponential smoothing, a particular smoothing constant α determines the weight given to the past information in arriving at the new estimate. Can $\alpha-$ values be used as a basis to identify stages of growth of products?

To answer the question, expected demand, the end product of exponential smoothing procedure, has to be expressed in terms of the new information added at any one point, and the previous information already in the system to that point. This derivation is shown in Table X. Expected demand is expressed in terms of three factors; (i) new demand, (ii) old average, and (iii) old trend. The coefficients of the three factors are expressed in terms of α. Since the particular α-value which satisfied the empirical data most closely can be determined empirically, if the *relative importance of new information and old* can be determined, this could be used as a basis to determine the *growth stage* of the particular product from its sales data.

When $\alpha = 0.1$, the coefficient of the new demand is 0.19, the coefficient of old average is 0.81, and the coefficient of old trend is 8.1. How important is the new demand with the respect to old average? We get the fraction 0.23. How important is the new demand with respect to old trend? We get 0.02. It means that the new demand does not really add very much to the information already contained in the system in the form of old average and old trend.

When $\alpha = 0.2$, the coefficient of old average is 0.64, that of new demand is 0.36, and that of old trend is 3.2. The importance of the new demand with respect to the old average is 0.56, and with respect to old trend is 0.11. Only when $\alpha = 0.5$ do we find that the contribution of the new demand with respect to the old average is 3.00, or, the *new demand*

TABLE X

STAGES-OF-GROWTH IDENTIFICATION BY α-VALUES IN
EXPONENTIAL SMOOTHING

Expected Demand $=$ New Average $\quad+\quad \dfrac{1-\alpha}{\alpha}$ New Trend

$\qquad = \alpha$ (New Demand) $\quad + \quad (1-\alpha)$ (Old Average)

$\qquad\qquad\qquad + \quad \dfrac{1-\alpha}{\alpha}$ [α (Current Trend $+ (1-\alpha)$ Old Trend]

Current Trend $\qquad =$ New Average $-$ $\qquad\qquad\qquad\qquad$ Old Average

$\qquad\qquad = \alpha$ (New Demand) $+ (1-\alpha)$ (Old Average) $-$ Old Average

$\qquad\qquad = \alpha$ (New Demand) $- \alpha$ (Old Average)

$\dfrac{1-\alpha}{\alpha} \cdot \alpha$ (Current Trend) $= (1-\alpha)$ [α (New Demand) $- \alpha$ (Old Average)]

$\qquad\qquad\qquad\qquad = (\alpha - \alpha^2)$ (New Demand) $+ (-\alpha + \alpha^2)$ (Old Average)

	New Demand	Old Average	Old Trend
	α	$1-\alpha$	$\dfrac{(1-\alpha)^2}{\alpha}$
	$\alpha - \alpha^2$	$-\alpha + \alpha^2$	
Expected Demand $=$	$(2\alpha - \alpha^2)$ New Demand $+$	$[1 - (2\alpha - \alpha^2)]$ Old Average $+$	$\dfrac{(1-\alpha)^2}{\alpha}$ Old Trend

information is three times as important as the old average; it is 1.5 times as
important as the old trend. When $\alpha = 0.8$, the new demand is 24 times as
important as the old average, and 19.2 times as important as the old trend.

When a product is in the stage of rapid growth, G_2, its rate of
growth is quite rapid, and therefore the new pieces of information are
crucial. When the product is in G_4, the stage of decline, the downward
movement is pretty much determined by the past data. Therefore, the role

TABLE XI

IMPORTANCE OF NEW DEMAND RELATIVE TO PRIOR DATA
CORRESPONDING TO DIFFERENT α-VALUES

Growth Stage	(1) α-Value	(2) Coefficient of NEW DEMAND	(3) Coefficient of OLD AVERAGE	(4) (2)/(3)	(5) Coefficient of OLD TREND	(6) (2)/(5)
G_4	0.1	0.19	0.81	0.23	8.10	0.02
	0.2	0.36	0.64	0.56	3.20	0.11
	0.3	0.51	0.49	1.04	1.63	0.31
	0.4	0.64	0.36	1.78	0.90	0.71
G_3	0.5	0.75	0.25	3.00	0.50	1.50
	0.6	0.84	0.16	5.25	0.27	3.11
	0.7	0.91	0.09	10.11	0.13	7.00
G_2	0.8	0.96	0.04	24.00	0.05	19.20
	0.9	0.99	0.01	99.00	0.01	99.00

of new demand is extremely insignificant. In between the two stages where new information is most important (G_2) and least important (G_4) lies the stage of maturation (G_3). During this stage, additional information is approximately as important as all the previous information in the system.

Thus the empirically determined α-values can serve to roughly divide the data analyzed into the three stages of growth: G_2, G_3, and G_4. In Table XI, $\alpha = 0.1$ through 0.4 are classified as G_4, $\alpha = 0.5$ through 0.7 as G_3, and $\alpha = 0.8$ through 0.9 as G_2.

PRODUCT LIFE CYCLE AND ORGANISMIC PERFORMANCE INDEX

Organisms sometimes seek a single, representative, measure of their overall performance. The life-cycle viewpoint of product history can be of significant assistance in bringing about the construction of such an index.

Such an index, in order to be useful, must provide a true estimate of the state-of-the-organism. Care should be exercised so that one does not get lost in the woods of this year's or last year's performance and miss the forest of the organism's long-term capabilities and limitations. This can happen only too easily if one looks only at the *prices and quantities* of the outputs (products), without a comprehensive view of the *growth and decay* of the scores of hundreds of products in the organism's portfolio.

The first stage, then is to determine the *life-cycle stage* of all major products of each component of the organism. A long-term prediction of the performance capabilities of the present product portfolio, whether by means of growth curves, orthogonal polynomials, or other equivalent analytical means, will permit the prediction of: (1) the highest dollar sales or quantity sales which may be expected of a particular product, (2) the time at which this may occur or has already occurred, and (3) the forecast for the next year(s). These computations are made on "At This Rate" basis. Use is made of only the past data on the assumption that the future can be seen from the past. The line staff, most closely associated with the performance of the outputs in the field, may very well know of new developments which could alter the assumption of such long-term predictions.

The second stage, therefore, is the discussion by the line management and the staff analysts of the interpretation of individual product life cycles provided by the analysis. After reconciling differences, if any, between field know-how and analytical know-how, customer wants must be studied. Each sales group can provide the breakdown of major products by major customers so that the life cycle of the product sales in each customer segment may be determined. Having agreed upon the life cycle analysis of both the product sales as a whole and product sales by customer wants, attention is turned inward to the relationship between prices and sales.

The third stage, therefore, starts with the sales groups providing detailed sales data on top sellers — quantity, freight, insurance, quantity discount, pricing agreements, pricing changes, gross dollar volume, and net dollar volume. Different elasticities of demand have then to be computed. Interpretation of elasticity measures with respect to *magnitude and sign* must be determined in conference between the analytical and line staff services.

The fourth stage studies the relationship between price changes and corresponding quantity changes of sales of substitute products within the different sales groups. As new substitutes are launched, the computations would be suitably enlarged. By this time a large number of products from each sales group have been selected to go into an *aggregate price index.* Errors in measurement are nearly always with us: they should be provided for. Errors of omission, leaving out of factors of consequence outside of the actual products selected, must also be corrected.

The fifth stage is the aggregation of the various pieces of analytical information developed. Mathematical statistical methods can be employed to answer the question: *How effective is the representation of several numbers by one?* — applied to both the various stages, and various operating units. The advantage of the mathematical statistical procedure is that the precise measure of representation of the different indices to represent a stage or a sales group can be determined. If the different prices should not be combined into one, that fact is also indicated.

The *method of principal components* is found to be applicable in examining the statistical validity of general index numbers in the following sense: How perfect is the representation, in this instance, of the prices and growth rates of all the sales groups by the Aggregate Price Index?

The method of principal components was first devised by Hotelling.[3] Wilks[4] presents the principal results in this area. Tintner[5] applied the method to determining the principal components of a set of production indices. He used as index of production for manufactured durable goods

---

[3]H. Hotelling, "Analysis of a Complex of Statistical Variables into Principal Components," *Journal of Educational Psychology,* vol. 24 (1933), pp. 417 - 441, 498 - 520.

[4]Samuel S. Wilks, *Mathematical Statistics* (New York: John Wiley & Sons, Inc., 1962), pp. 564 - 573.

[5]G. Tintner, "Some applications of Multivariate Analysis to Economic Data," *Journal of the American Statistical Association,* vol. 41 (1946), pp. 482ff.

(X_1), and for nondurable goods (X_2), and so on:

$X_1 =$ manufactured durable goods in the United States

$X_2 =$ nondurable goods in the United States

$X_3 =$ minerals in the United States

$X_4 =$ agricultural products in the United States

He obtained the function u which minimizes the error variances and which also has the maximum sum of squares of correlation coefficients with all the variables (while its own variance is 1).

The factor "production in general" (represented by the function u) seems to account for the most of the variance of X_4, as well as most of the variances of all other variables.

The tentative economic interpretation of these results would appear to be as follows: It seems that the fluctuations in the four indices may be reasonably well represented by one factor. This general "factor" would account for more than three-fourths of the total variance of the individual production indices.[6]

The sixth stage is the conference on *Sales Group* and *Stage Indices*. Where the representation by one index is inadequate, and analysis indicates other alternatives, they have to be decided upon in conference.

The seventh stage is the computation of the aggregate price index from the different sales group and stage indices, the analysis of its implications and limitations, and consequent policy recommendations to top management of the sales groups and the organism.

These time series disclose the *long-term* performance potential as revealed by the empirical data on hand. They are by no means directly or finally applicable to the rate of growth of component products, or of component industrial units over a period of any length, particularly in the *short term*. An overall industry-performance index suggests its stage of growth, provides a perspective of its performance potentials, within which the strength and weakness of individual components of the industry, over time periods of shorter duration, may be usefully compared and contrasted.

PRODUCT LIFE CYCLE — NICB DATA

The stages of growth are identified in the computer program by means of α-values empirically determined successively as new information

---

[6] G. Tintner, *Econometrics* (New York: John Wiley & Sons, Inc., 1954), p. 112.

is added. If, however, growth curves were fitted to periods of data, they could provide a *long-term* view of the performance of the data as well as is seen on the basis of the available observations, as distinguished from the *short-term* observations provided by the α-values of the computer program.

The National Industrial Conference Board (NICB) studied over 30 industries — agriculture, fuels, metals, nonmetals, transportation, and others, using a Gompertz curve of the form:

$$X_t = AB^{c^t}$$

where X_t = value of dependent variable at time t, most often production or consumption in the study

t = independent variable, in this case time measured in years

A,B,C = constants to be evaluated from the given time series

The logarithmic form of the equation above is:
$$\log X_t = \log A + C^t \log B$$

In this form, $\log A$, the first constant to be evaluated, is the asymptote, the value which $\log X_t$ approaches but never attains. If C is between 0 and 1, C^t will become smaller and smaller as t increases. Consequently, $C^t \log B$ will become smaller and smaller, and $\log X_t$ will approach $\log A$. $\log B$, the second constant to be evaluated, represents the difference between $\log X_t$, when $t = 0$ and the asymptote, $\log A$. When $t = 0$, $C^t = 1$ and $\log X_t - \log A = \log B$. The third constant is C, which represents the ratio between successive first differences of $\log X$.

The four features of the curves fitted in this manner are: (1) A rate of growth that declines continuously, (2) A nonnegative growth rate, (3) The existence of a "critical year" or point of inflection. The computed differences increase year by year and then at some point start to decline, and (4) The asymptotic nature of the growth curve — it has a value that the curve constantly approaches, but never attains.

In Table XII some of the results are shown. We find wheat production had its critical year in 1886, and the rate of growth in 1948–58 was 0.4 percent. In the life-cycle terminology we would say that wheat production is in the stage of decline or G_4. Similarly bituminous coal production had the critical year in 1897, and its rate of growth in 1948–58 was 0.3 percent. Lead consumption attained maturity in 1916, and grew at a rate of 0.4 percent in 1948–58. Portland cement production had a critical year in 1920 and a rate of growth of 0.8 percent in 1948–58.

In contrast with the rate of growth in the stage of decline, we find soybean production zooming at a rate of 7.6 percent in 1948–58. The critical year, as judged by the past growth, was placed at 1960. It should be remembered that the forecast was made at a time period prior to 1960; hence, there may be revisions at a later date in the light of experience. Primary aluminum production also grew at a high rate, of 7.5 percent, in 1948–58. Its upward growth is expected to go on until the year 2022. Life insurance in force is expected to go on until the year 2522; its rate of growth in 1948–58 was 6.7 percent. The monthly average of asphalt production is also expected to reach the maturation point sometime in the future, the year 2069, its recent growth having been 6.0 percent. Gross physical output (U.S.), based on 1929 prices, is scheduled to continue its upward trend until the year 2090; the recent growth rate was 2.6 percent in 1948–58. The data in this case started in 1889, were converted to index number form with 1929 as base. The series is expressed in fixed prices. These series are obviously in G_2 stage.

Cotton consumpton reached its point of maturation in the year 1916, and registered a growth of 1.0 percent during 1948–58. Pig iron production had a critcal year of 1919, with a rate of growth of 1.1 percent during 1948–58. This is reflected in the steel ingot production which

TABLE XII

"CRITICAL YEAR" AND PERCENTAGE RATE OF GROWTH FOR PRODUCTS — NATIONAL INDUSTRIAL CONFERENCE BOARD

STAGE	PRODUCT	"Critical Year" (Maturation Point)	1948–58 Percent Rate of Growth
G_4 Stage	Wheat production	1886	0.4
	Bituminous coal production	1897	0.3
	Lead consumption	1916	0.4
	Portland cement production	1920	0.8
G_2 Stage	Soybean production	1960	7.6
	Aluminum (primary) production	2022	7.5
	Life insurance in force	2522	6.7
	Asphalt production — monthly average	2069	6.0
	Gross physical output (1929 prices)	2090	2.6
G_3 Stage	Cotton consumption	1916	1.0
	Pig-iron production	1919	1.1
	Steel ingot production	1930	1.6
	Energy fuel production	1929	1.3
	Railway ton-miles	1917	1.0

Basic source: J. Frank Gaston, *Growth Patterns in Industry: A Reexamination*, National Industrial Conference Board (New York, 1961), Table 2.

reached its critical year in 1930, and had a rate of growth during 1948–58 of 1.6 percent. The steel castings and ingots series covers 90 years starting in 1870. Energy fuel production and railway ton-miles are two other series which attained their critical years respectively in 1929 and 1917, and had respective rates of growth of 1.3 and 1.0 percent for the period 1948–58. Compared with the 2.6 percent gross physical output growth rate, we would want to classify the cotton consumption, pig-iron production, steel ingot production, energy fuel production, and railway ton-miles series in the stage of maturation in the life-cycle terminology.

This division of the series, shown in Table XII, into three stages is admittedly an arbitrary one. Gross physical output could be used as a basis for arriving at the growth-of-stage determination of different products and services. More significant than the 2.6 percent growth in 1948–58 is the critical year, fixed at 2090. Any series which indicates an upward trend for another hundred and odd years should certainly be classified as being in the rapid growth stage, G_2. Based on this criterion, the classification of soybean production, with its critical year 1960, in stage G_2 will be questionable. However, the point of maturation must be tempered with the rate of growth over a selected period, as 1948–58. We can be more definite with respect to history. Therefore, series which had their critical years before 1930, or about 30 to 50 years ago can certainly be considered to have reached maturity.

There will be little question that wheat production, which attained its maturation in the year 1886 and showed a rate of growth of 0.4 percent in 1948–58, is in the stage of decline, stage G_4.

There will be the question of statistical significance of difference between borderline percentages. For instance, is 0.8 percent growth of Portland cement production significantly lower than 1 percent growth of cotton consumption, so that Portland cement is placed in G_4 and cotton consumption in G_3? A satisfactory rule for such borderline cases can be obtained empirically based on the desirability of wrong classification, of G_3 as G_4 and G_4 as G_3, depending on the gravity of such misclassification.

It is clear that a reasonable and consistent method of classification can be used to arrange the long-term predictions of performance of the different time series. Both the rate of growth percentage and the point of maturation need be taken into account in assigning such a state of growth to a time series.

ELEMENTS OF PERIODIC TABLE OF PRODUCT DIVERSIFICATION

The basic unifying element in the periodic table is the weighted growth by *product* and weighted growth by *stage*. The same product will register different percentages of growth in different years: and correspondingly, different percentages of contribution to the total organismic sales. Arranging of the percentage of product sales by its contributions to the total organismic sale gives a weighted percentage of the sales growth by product. There are different products offered by the same organism. Since these different products grow at a different rate from year to year, and correspondingly contribute differently to the total organismic sales, index for the organism's satiability of outside world wants can be derived from the performance of different products by stage. Thus, products can be classified each year, or convenient time period, into the four stages of growth.

The major elements of the Periodic Table of Product Diversification are: (1) product satiability; and (2) want intensity. A product is intended to satisfy at least one want, and its ability to satisfy is referred to as the product's satiability, its *S-Index* (page 129). The consumer has different wants, some of them more urgent than others, How vital is the want satisfied by the particular product is referred to as want intensity, its *V-Index*.

V — INDEX

The vital nature of wants may be measured in different ways. One approach would be the *negative consequences of nonfulfillment* of the need. In order to employ this criterion, the role of a transistor used in a space capsule has to be compared with, say, the role of a transistor used in a television set. If the transistor in the space capsule were not there, it would probably involve the failure of the entire mission; whereas the absence of the transistor in the television set would merely hold up the TV-viewing until the particular transistor was replaced. Similarly, a chemical used in food and kindred products might be more vital than the same chemical used in soap manufacture. *The only requirement of the V-Index is the possibility of consistently ranking the vital nature of the needs satisfied by the same product.* The most vital want may be referred to as V_1, the next most vital as V_2, and so on until V_n for the least vital of the needs satisfied by the same product.

A second criterion of the V-Index would be the *negative consequence of malfunctioning.* Repair in outer space is generally more difficult than repairs in the living room. Therefore the malfunctioning of a transistor in a space capsule would be more difficult to correct than that of a transistor in a home television set. The more crucial the role of the component to the particular system, the more damaging will be the consequences of malfunctioning. The failure of the automatic reentry instrument system in Astronaut Gordon Cooper's space flight did not abort his mission, because he could employ manual controls. The automatic system thus could afford to malfunction without vital damage to the mission, because, not being crucial, its performance could be allowed a certain margin of error. Margin for error in performance can thus be used as a criterion for the V-Index.

A third criterion could be the contribution of the successful performance of the product to the accomplishment of the overall objective of the organism. Thus, the dependable performance of the transistor in the space capsule facilitates the accomplishment of a space mission; the dependable performance of a transistor in the television set aids the viewing pleasure for several evenings. The importance of the accomplishment of the objective is derived from the significance of the objective to the organism itself. Whether or not the success of a space mission is more important than the feasibility of family entertainment is a moot question. A yardstick which would meaningfully encompass outer and inner spaces, so to speak, should have an extraterrestrial dimension which would simultaneously stand outside of both the entities involved. We shall have to introduce "ought" propositions, saying that satisfaction in the inner space ought to be more important than accomplishment in the outer space, or that accomplishment in outer space ought to be more important than satisfaction in inner space, and so on. We may soon find out that we cannot have the one without the other: The deprivation of relaxation facilities at home may impair the efficiency of the scientist who has to work on the conquest of space; continued nonaccomplishment in space may lead to curtailment of the space projects, and consequently decreased demand for the services of the scientist, who may not be able to afford a TV set for relaxation.

We shall, therefore, not attempt to make interorganismic considerations of objectives. We shall investigate the vital nature of the wants of the same customer satisfied by the same product. The customer, whether an industry, an individual, an institution, or any other equivalent entity, will be considered able to judge the *relative importance of the different needs* of his own satisfied by the same product.

Price Elasticity of Demand

Turning from criteria of V-Index to its measurement, one measure of the vital nature of the want satisfied is the *responsiveness of the demand* for the product to changes in price. Demand for a product is always demand for a product at a price. Since the money spent for the purchase of a particular product cannot simultaneously be used for the purchase of some other product, the fraction of the money spent for different products can be considered an indication of the relative importance the customer attaches to the several products. These expenditures are undertaken successively over time, corresponding to varying sets of prices; the different percentages of total expenditure indicate the changing importance of the particular products at different prices. Thus, the demand for wheat would probably remain more stable over a wide price range than the demand for chewing gum over a similarly wide price range. The latter is more responsive to changes in price than the former. The fraction

$$\frac{\text{Proportionate change in quantity demanded}}{\text{Proportionate change in price}}$$

known as Price Elasticity of Demand, can be used to assess the degree of vital nature of the want satisfied.

In Table XIII, the elements of V-Index of an output are identified. Offhand, one would consider food, shelter, and clothing to be most vital for an individual consumer. If these are at one end of the scale, marked "most vital needs," entertainment efforts could be at the other end of the scale, marked "least vital needs." Assuming that there is a single product which can be used in all of these areas of need, what is the V-Index of the output in these different areas of need?

Penalty Measure for Unavailability,
Penalty Measure for Malfunctioning

In order to construct a scale of V-Index, we must fix the maximum and the minimum values with respect to the accomplishment of the objective. For instance, the maximum value for satisfying food needs is placed at 500. If, however, the output malfunctions and, say, turns to food poison, the penalty is placed at 100. Two types of penalties for failure were identified earlier: (1) penalty if an output is not available; and (2) penalty if an output malfunctions. In the illustration in Table XIII, if the particular output were not available to satisfy food needs, the penalty is put at 100. If the output malfunctions, then the same amount of penalty is assessed. But the penalty for not having the output for shelter purposes is rated at 80 instead of 100, as in the case of food. Similarly, the penalty for malfunctioning of an output with respect to shelter is placed at 75, as compared with 100 for food. While the penalties for unavailability and malfunctioning are equal with respect to food, it is not so with respect to shelter and clothing. For both shelter and clothing, the penalty for

TABLE XIII

ELEMENTS OF V-INDEX OF AN OUTPUT (PRODUCT)
ILLUSTRATIVE WEIGHTING ON A SCALE OF VITAL NATURE OF WANTS

WANTS ➡ ⬇ ACCOMPLISHMENT	Vital Nature of Wants				
	Most Vital V_1-Food	Shelter	Clothing	Education	Least Vital, V_{10}-Enter- tainment
Penalty if output is not available	100	80	70	50	10
Penalty if output malfunctions ...	100	75	65	50	10
Reward if output accomplishes objective	500	160	210	400	10
Penalty for unavailability	$\frac{100}{500} \times 100 = 20$	16	14	10	2
Penalty for malfunctioning	20	15	13	10	2
Reward for good performance ..	100	32	42	80	2
Total Score	140	63	69	100	6
Rank Order	V_1	V_4	V_3	V_2	V_{10}

malfunctioning is placed slightly lower than that for unavailability. It is assumed, not altogether arbitrarily, that to have rotten food is as bad as to have no food at all, while a leaky roof is not as bad as having no roof at all.

Reward Measures

What is the significance to the objective of the organism as a whole if the particular output accomplishes the objective of a component of the organism? Conversely, what is the penalty for unavailability? In the case of food, this ratio is $500/100 = 5$; shelter, $160/80 = 2$; clothing, $210/70 = 3$; education, $400/50 = 8$; and entertainment, $10/10 = 1$. Similarly, the values of the fraction (penalty for malfunctioning)/(penalty for unavailability) are, respectively, for food, $100/100 = 1$; shelter, $75/80 = 0.938$; clothing, $65/70 = 0.929$; education, $50/50 = 1$; and entertainment, $10/10 = 1$. We notice thus that the essential elements of the V-Index of an output are: (1) Penalty for unavailability; (2) Penalty for malfunctioning; (3) Reward for good performance; (4) (penalty for malfunctioning)/ (penalty for unavailability); and (5) (reward for good performance)/(penalty for unavailability).

These illustrative *values* can be converted into *scores*. The highest reward value, indicating the significance of the accomplishment of the objective to the organism may be used as the common denominator: in this instance, 500 for food. Expressing each of the entries in the Table in terms of this denominator, we find that the reward for good performance in food has a score of 100; penalty for unavailability in food has a score of 20; and penalty for malfunctioning in food also has a score of 20. These three add to a total score of 140. Similarly, shelter has a penalty score for unavailability of 16, 15 for malfunctioning, and reward score for good performance of 32. The total comes to 63. Based on the aggregate of these total scores, we find that the vital index for food is V_1 for the highest score of 140; V_2 for education for the second highest score of 100; V_3 for clothing for the third highest score of 69; V_4 for shelter for the fourth highest score of 63; and V_{10} for entertainment for a score of 6.

S-INDEX

Cross-Elasticity of Demand

The reward for good performance, considered in Table XIII, is a function not only of the vital nature of wants, but also of the ability of the outputs to satisfy the given want. Price elasticity of demand was discussed as a measure of the vital nature of wants. Cross-elasticity of demand is a kindred concept, relevant to the satiability of wants. If Product A is not giving sufficient satisfaction to the customer, Product B claims to meet the same want, there is a possibility that the customer may shift from A to B. While the initial shift may be caused by the consumer's interest in experimenting, if the shift is sustained over the long run, one may hypothesize that the ability of Product A to satisfy the want has been found unsatisfactory by the customer, who, therefore, shifted to Product B. Similar to the price elasticity of demand, cross-elasticity of demand is

$$\frac{\text{Proportionate change in the quantity of B demanded}}{\text{Proportionate change in the price of A}}$$

Since different products of the same manufacturer may satisfy similar wants, cross-elasticity of demand at different points in time, and also over specified periods of time, would be a helpful indicator to the organism as to how well it is doing with respect to the customers' wants. Successive values of cross-elasticity may well indicate to the organism to shift production from Product A to Product B.

Growth Curves and Longer-Term Satiability

While cross-elasticity of demand highlights the output's satiability of customer wants at a particular time or at particular time points, *growth curves* of the product provide insights into *longer-term performance* of the outputs in satisfying customer wants. The percentage of growth in the total exchange (sales) of output (product) over successive periods in time is one measure of such satisfaction. The initial period of exposure of the output to the outside world by the organism is likely to be a period of slow growth. A basic effort involved in the early stages is the very *idea* of want satisfaction by that particular product. Prior to the availability of headache remedies without prescription, the first headache pill would have had to counter the resistance of potential customers to the very idea that such remedies could be dispensed without prescription. The initial resistance was overcome, and people began to get used to the idea of headache pills being available. Then, similar pills could be sold for any number of ailments, minor, and even some major. If Anacin were the first pill to be offered as a headache remedy, its early sales growth would indeed have been extremely restricted. However, once the idea caught on, the stage was set for Anacin sales to grow rapidly. Furthermore, another tablet, Bufferin, could enter the market and cash in on the successful initiation that was accomplished by the sales of the first headache remedy, Anacin.

Following G_1, the stage of infancy, G_2, the stage of rapid growth, will lead to G_3, the stage of maturation, and subsequent decline in G_4. The process of recovery of investment in the particular product has to be accomplished primarily in the rapid growth stage, and secondarily in the maturation stage. The inner workings of a product with respect to the market must thus be determined accurately to permit early planning of effective action. Such a determination is important not only from the point of view of a particularly good product, but also from the point of view of the organism as a whole. Should the majority of the products of the organism be in the maturation stage, it should be recognized that the organism is fast approaching the edge of a steep precipice. The remedial action would have had to be instituted long before this particular time period, because research and development efforts take considerable investment in time, talent, and money. By the same token, if the majority of the products of the organism are in the rapid growth stage, the earning from such sales would be substantial. However, this sales performance by itself should not be an invitation to complacency. On the contrary, it should be taken as an early indication to the organism that following the seven fat years, there are going to be seven lean years. The time to prepare for the lean years is the fat years.

Satiability Measures,
Significance Measures

The determination of the particular S-Index of the sales of the output (product) to the market by the organism is important in two respects: (1) as a satiability measure of the product to all its customers, (2) as a significance measure of product sales to organism. We see from Table XIV that the satiability measure comprises: (i) price elasticity of demand of the product, (ii) percentage of growth of the product sales from year to year or other suitable time periods, (iii) stage of growth of the product sales.

While these measures relate to the total product sales to all the customers, any valid prediction of the direction of the sales of the product would necessitate closer scrutiny of major customers of the product. It is to the extent that major customers are satisfied by the particular product that its growth in the future is assured. To identify the satiability measure affecting major customers, we ask the questions: How important is each customer in the total sales picture of the product? How important is the particular product purchase to the customer? and How rapidly has the purchase of the particular product by the major customer(s) been growing during the past several time periods?

TABLE XIV

ELEMENTS OF S-INDEX OF AN OUTPUT (PRODUCT):
RECOGNITION OF ALTERNATIVE SOURCE(S) OF SIMILAR WANT
SATISFACTION AND SIGNIFICANCE OF
OUTPUT ACTIVITY TO ORGANISM

SATIABILITY MEASURE AND SIGNIFICANCE TIME (Year)	Y_0	Y_1	Y_2	Y_3		Y_0	Y_1	Y_2	Y_3
A. Satiability of total product sales to all customers					B. Satiability of total substitute product sales to all customers				
Quantity					Quantity				
Dollars					Cross elasticity				
Price elasticity					Percent of growth				
Stage of growth					Stage of growth				
C. Significance to organism of total product sales					D. Satiability of partial product sales to major customers				
Percent of organismic sales					Percent of total product sales				
Weighted percent of growth					Percent of total customers purchase				
					Percent of product growth				

No product operates in a vacuum. It competes with other products to satisfy customer wants. This competition may very well come in part from other outputs of the same organism. And the customer for his part will shift from one output to another, be it offered by the same organism or competing organisms, depending on the advantages offered. Thus the satiability measure of the product cannot be considered meaningful without a corresponding satiability measure of *substitute outputs* (*SP*-products). As discussed earlier, cross-elasticity of demand for a substitute product would be a relevant measure to indicate the strength and weakness of the position of the product. In addition to the satiability of an output (product) to all the customers, it is thus important to study the satiability to major customers, customers who carefully weigh the product and substitute products in terms of want satisfaction.

What do the total product sales mean to the organism as a whole? One measure of such significance is the total sales of the product expressed as a fraction of the total organismic sales. This fraction can be used to weigh the percentage of growth over successive time periods of the total product sales. The measure would put in perspective the strength and weakness of the particular product in the products of the organism as a whole.

Prices of the particular product will vary as advances in technology permit the organism to pass on the fruits of technological advances to customers in the form of price reductions. The technological advancement pertaining to the product itself will indicate the appropriateness of price strategy in its own domain. However, translating the cost reductions afforded by the technological innovations will be determined by the price reduction policies with respect to other outputs of the organism as well, which are also recipients of savings by technological advancement.

EMPIRICAL ELEMENTS OF PRODUCT LIFE CYCLE

We identified in Table XIII a particular classification of Customer Industries with respect to the vital nature of wants. Food was classified as most vital, designated by V_1, Education V_2, Clothing V_3, and so on. However, if all the exchange (sales) of an output (product) were made to only food industries, the relative vital nature of wants of the customers within the food industry itself might be ranked by the total units of sale to the segments of the food industry. Thus, if the sales of Product I to Customer Industry I and Customer Industry II, shown in Figure 16 (page 133), were made to the food industry, then the sales to Customer Industry I would rank higher than those to Customer Industry II, by reason

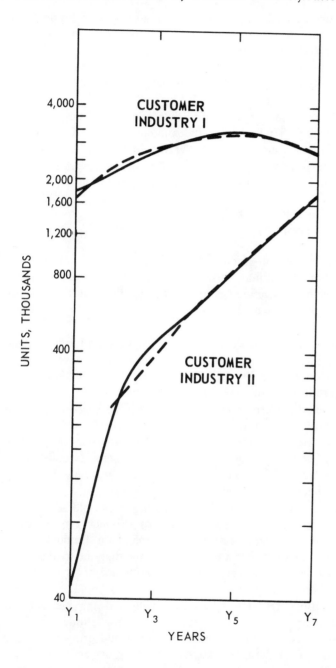

Figure 16. SALE OF PRODUCT I TO TWO MAJOR CUSTOMER INDUSTRIES (YEAR Y_1-Y_7).

of the absolute units of sales involved. Let us assume that Product I is sold to Customer Industry III with sales units less than Customer Industry II, and Customer Industry IV with sales less than Customer Industry I. Thus, the ordering in terms of the V-Index would be: Customer Industry I — V_{11}, Customer Industry II — V_{13}, Customer Industry III — V_{14}, and Customer Industry IV — V_{12}.

We shall now turn to the study of data relating to sales of certain products to see if the V-Index and S-Index points of view facilitate the understanding of product sales to make better decisions.

For this purpose, we shall first study the sales data, *qua* sales data and second, the sales data from the V and S-Indexes point of view.

PROJECTED PERFORMANCE OF PRODUCT GROUP AND COMPONENT PRODUCTS

Consider the case of Product Group I, the total sales of which in the year Y_1 are about 24 million units. Data for years Y_1–Y_7 are available, on the basis of which a projection has to be made for the next five years. A five-year plan comprising years Y_8–Y_{12} is to be submitted to the management and approved.

A major component of Product Group I is Product I, which alone accounted for 17 million units out of the 24 million units in year Y_1. In order to chart a course for Product Group I, a clearer picture of the performance of Product I would be of great value.

The projected performance of Product I can be based directly on the total volume of sales of the product in the years Y_1–Y_7. Such a projection extends into the future a *gross entity*. The procedure is adequate if the gross entity itself is composed of homogeneous units, or units whose performances are sufficiently homogeneous in time, traveling in nearly identical paths as that of the gross entity itself.

As it turns out, the particular product has been sold to different industries, the components of the total sales of Product I being quite heterogeneous in their nature and extent of demand for Product I. The traditional approach to the problem consisted of extending the total sales of Product I linearly into the future, with little reference to the different markets for the product.

The operations research approach highlighted the necessity to identify the behavior of the component markets for Product I. The projected performances of the component markets would provide a firmer basis of comparison than the mere extension of the gross entity, the total sales of Product I.

In Figure 16 the sale of Product I to two major Customer Industries is shown. Customer Industry I has been purchasing between 2 and 3 million units of Product I during the years Y_1–Y_7. During the same period, Customer Industry II demand demonstrated a phenomenal rise from 40,000 units to about 1.5 million units. What is the nature of purchases by these two Customer Industries in the years Y_8–Y_{12}?

Standard Industrial Classification

A word about the Customer Industries is in order. These customer identifications were selected for their effective classificatory nature.

> The Structure of the (Standard Industrial) Classification makes it possible to classify establishments by industry on either a two-digit, a three-digit, or a four-digit basis, according to the degree of detail in information which may be needed.... An "establishment" is an economic unit which produces goods or services — for example, a farm, a mine, a factory, a store. In most instances, the establishment is at a single physical location; and it is engaged in only one, or predominantly one, type of economic activity for which an industry code is applicable.[7]

The highest hierarchy of the Standard Industrial Classification (SIC), is Division. Division A comprises agriculture, forestry, and fisheries; Division B, mining; Division C, contract construction; Division D, manufacturing; Division E, transportation, communication, electric, gas and sanitary services; Division F, wholesale and retail trade; Division G, finance, insurance and real estate; Division H, services; Division I, Government; and Division J, nonclassifiable establishments.

Thus the sale of Product I to any segment of the United States economy can be identified under these Major Divisions. These Divisions themselves are divided into *Major Groups*. Major Groups 19 – 39, for instance, are components of Division D: manufacturing. Major Group 19 consists of ordnance and accessories establishments; Major Group 20, food and kindred products; and so on until Major Group 39, miscellaneous manufacturing industries which are not classifiable under any of the preceding manufacturing establishments.

The Major Groups themselves are further subdivided into Groups — Minor Groups, if one were to make a distinction here. *Group Number* 201 is a subdivision of the Major Group 20 and relates to meat products

---

[7] Executive Office of the President, Bureau of the Budget, *Standard Industrial Classification Manual* (Washington, D.C.: U.S. Government Printing Office, 1957) pp. 1 - 3.

establishments; Group Number 202 dairy products establishments; 203 canning and preserving fruits, vegetables and sea foods; 204 grain mill products; 205 bakery products; 206 sugar; 207 confectionery and related products; 208 beverage industries; and 209 miscellaneous food preparations and kindred products. Thus if Product I were sold to the dairy industry for use in dairy products, that sale could be identified as a sale to Group Number 202. If sales were made to bakery product establishments, those would be classified under Group Number 205.

The groups, or *Minor* Groups — to distinguish them from the Major Groups — are themselves subdivided into *Industries*. Thus Minor Group Number 202: dairy products establishments are divided into 2021: creamery butter, 2022 natural cheese, 2023 condensed and evaporated milk; 2024 ice cream and frozen desserts; 2025 special dairy products; and 2026 fluid milk. Similarly Group Number 205; bakery products establishments are further subdivided into 2051; bread and other bakery products, except biscuit, crackers, and pretzels, and 2052: biscuit, crackers, and pretzels establishments.

Given the objective of projecting the performance of Products Group I in the years Y_8–Y_{12}, in order to prepare and launch development programs comprising the entire Product Group I, it was found meaningful to investigate the significant segments of the sale of Product I. The method of orthogonal polynomials to fit the most appropriate mathematical curve to the raw data has advantages which recommend its employment, particularly in the case of manual curve-fitting.

Orthogonal Polynomial Curve-Fitting

The straight-line and four other polynomials are:

$$\text{First-degree (straight-line) } Y = a + bx$$
$$\text{Second-degree (parabola) } Y = a + bx + cx^2$$
$$\text{Third-degree (cubic) } Y = a + bx + cx^2 + dx^3$$
$$\text{Fourth-degree (quartic) } Y = a + bx + cx^2 + dx^3 + ex^4$$
$$\text{Fifth-degree (quintic) } Y = a + bx + cx^2 + dx^3 + ex^4 + fx^5$$

A minor disadvantage of polynomial equations of the type described is that each additional constant added to an equation requires that some of the constants previously obtained be abandoned and new constants computed to take their place. Thus, a second-degree curve uses the same value for b as a straight line, but requires a different value for a; a third-degree curve uses the same values for a and c as a second-degree curve, but requires a new value for b; a fourth-degree curve uses the same values for b

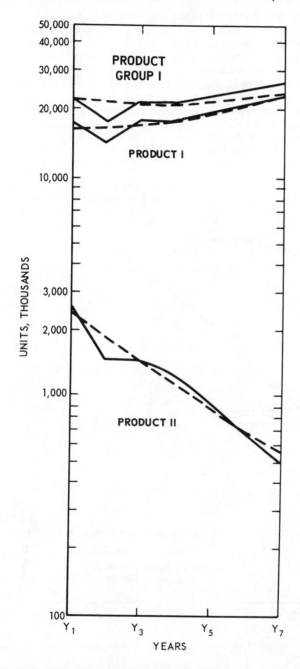

Figure 17. SALE OF PRODUCTS I AND II IN PRODUCT GROUP I (YEARS Y_1 - Y_7).

and *d* as a third-degree curve, but new values must be calculated for *a* and *c*; and so on. *Orthogonal polynomial* equations involve a transformation of such a nature that, as new constants are added, the old constants remain the same. Such equations are very convenient to use, since we merely build up our equation by adding new constants until a satisfactory fit is obtained and simultaneous solution of equations is avoided. There is thus no lost motion, and the labor involved becomes progressively less than that required to fit a curve by the ordinary method for equations of third-degree and higher. The trend values obtained by the two methods are exactly the same.[8]

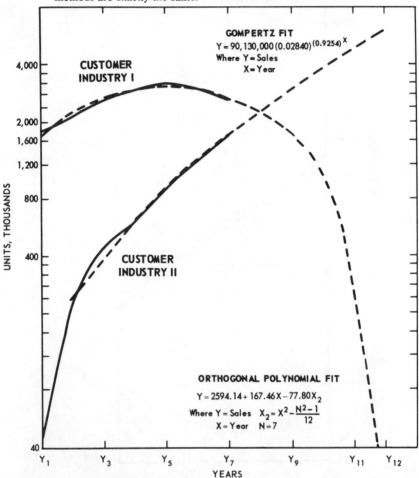

Figure 18. SALE OF PRODUCT I TO TWO MAJOR CUSTOMER INDUSTRIES (YEARS Y_1 - Y_{12}).

[8]F. E. Croxton and D. J. Cowden, *Applied Statistics* (New York: Prentice-Hall, Inc., 1955), p. 289.

We now consider the result of orthogonal polynomial fitting to two sets of sales data. The first is the sales of Product I to *only two* of its customers, viz; Customer Industry I and Customer Industry II, during the years Y_1-Y_7 (Figure 16). The projected performance of the sales in the years Y_8-Y_{12} to these two customers of Product I is shown in Figure 18.

The second is the sales of Product Group I and two of its components, viz. Product I and Product II, to all their customers during

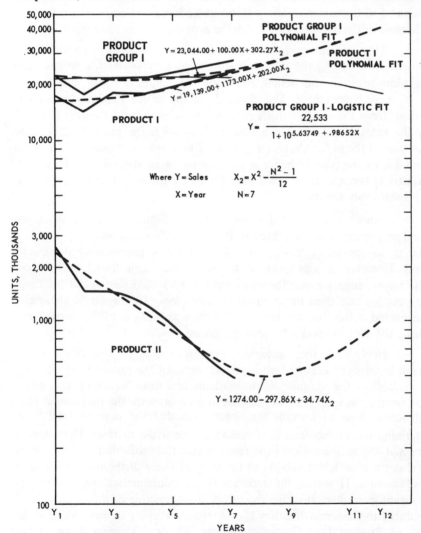

Figure 19. ORTHOGONAL POLYNOMIALS FITTED TO SALES OF PRODUCTS I AND II AND THE ENTIRE PRODUCT GROUP I

the years Y_1–Y_7 shown in Figure 17. The projected performance into the years Y_8–Y_{12} of these Products to all their customers is shown in Figure 19.

Utterly unexpected results are seen in the sales of Product I to Customer Industry I. As opposed to the traditional projection into the future, more or less on a linear basis, the sales of Product I to Customer Industry I are seen to be destined to a drastic plummeting down, which is particularly marked beginning with year Y_{10}. With respect to sales of Product I to Customer Industry II, an exceptionally strong upward trend is indicated for the five years for which the projection is made (Figure 19).

The particular mathematical function fitting the raw data was chosen from among the different orthogonal polynomial fits so the least deviation between the actual and expected values for the data period Y_1–Y_7 may be obtained. The closeness of the fit for Product Group I is obvious from Figure 19, which projects the sales data of Product Group I for the years Y_1–Y_7 shown in Figure 17 through the years Y_8–Y_{12}: The closeness of the fit for Customer Industry I purchase of Product I is obvious from Figure 18. the orthogonal polynomial fit to the sales to Customer Industry II is not as close as the fit to Customer Industry I; nevertheless, the fit is reasonably accurate.

Another unexpected result is seen in Figure 19 where an orthogonal polynomial has been fitted to Product II. From all accounts, the data relating to the years Y_1–Y_7 strongly indicate a pronounced downward trend. However, the polynomial fit which has been found to be most satisfactory, suggests that the downward trend would *flatten out* by about the year Y_9 and then begin to *climb thereafter*. This again is an utterly unexpected result on the basis of intuitive extension of the experience during the data years Y_1–Y_7 into the future.

How should these unexpected results be treated? The answer would lie not in terms of reasonableness or otherwise of the projected results, but on the basis of the adequacy of the mathematical fit to the data points which have been observed. Thus we see that in each instance the polynomial fit is sufficiently close to warrant the observation that the mathematical fit is describing the phenomena in a reasonably accurate manner. Once this is accepted, the mathematical logic requires that the projection into the future be also given sufficient validity as far as consistency of the mathematical fit would permit. However, the accuracy of the mathematical formulation by no means guarantees that there would be a plummeting down in the sales of Product I to Customer Industry I, or a strong sweeping upward trend in the sales of Product I to Customer Industry II, or a slowing down of the pronounced downward trend in the sales of Product II by year Y_9 and then a distinct, upward trend. But what it does state is that, if the particular mathematical curve is an acceptable description of past data, then the projections based on it should be permitted to call attention to some phenomena in the real world even when they appear contrary to common sense.

Turning to the practical implications, should or should not the product manager of Products I and II be given permission to pursue expansion programs based on predictions of the future?

Utterly unexpected turn of events are projected by the mathematical formulations. The contribution of the analysis here has been to call attention to the fact that there may be inherent factors which are not immediately visible that suggest these unexpected behaviors in the sales of Products I and II, whether in *total*, or in terms of their *components*. Should further study of the influences which help determine the sales of Product I to Customer Industry I disclose a serious weakening in the future, the Product Manager may want to accentuate the strong potentials in sales of Product I to Customer Industry II in order to compensate for the weakness in Customer Industry I. Perhaps the elements of strength in Customer Industry II are cultivable in Customer Industry I demand for Product I.

Let us now study the same sales data from the points of view respectively of V-Index and S-Index.

EMPIRICAL ELEMENTS OF V-INDEX

Product I Sales, Presumably to 4 Customer Industry Components Of Major Industry Group 20

The extent of satisfaction derived by the respective customers from the purchase of Product I can be measured by the fraction that the total purchase value of Product I represents in the total purchase of similar items by the customer industry. Thus if Product I is purchased as an input to manufacture some other products, the denominator would be the total expenditure on similar inputs. Measuring the vital nature of the want satisfied by Product I, it is important to notice how the significance of the product in the total purchases of the industry itself changes over successive time periods. It is important also to know the contribution of Product I to Industry Group V_1, of which the Customer Industries V_{11}, V_{12}, and V_{13}, V_{14} are components.

We note in Table XV that in the year Y_1, 22.8 percent of the total sales of Product I was made to Industry Group V_1. The corresponding fraction in the year Y_2 was 26.2 percent, and in Y_3, 26.9 percent. How were

TABLE XV

ILLUSTRATIVE EMPIRICAL ELEMENTS OF V-INDEX OF PRODUCT I (FIGURE 16) PRESUMABLY SOLD TO FOUR CUSTOMER INDUSTRIES IN MAJOR GROUP 20

TIME (Year) → V-INDEX MEASURES	Percent, Y_1	Percent, Y_2	Percent, Y_3	DIRECTION
V_1 — FOOD AND KINDRED PRODUCTS				
Product I Sales to Major Group 20				
Major Group 20 *total* purchases of kindred products	0.009	0.011	0.013	←
Product I Sales to Major Group 20				
Total Product I sales	22.8	26.2	26.9	
V_{11} — CUSTOMER INDUSTRY I				
Product I Sales to Component I of Major Group 20				
Major Group 20 Component I's *Total* Purchase of kindred products	0.049	0.064	0.078	←
Product I Sales to Component I of Major Group 20				
Total Product I sales	14.3	15.5	16.0	
V_{12} — CUSTOMER INDUSTRY IV				
Product I Sales to Component IV of Major Group 20				
Major Group 20 Component IV's *Total* purchase of kindred products	0.009	0.003	0.004	
Product I Sales to Component IV of Major Group 20				
Total Product I sales	5.7	5.6	5.5	
V_{13} — CUSTOMER INDUSTRY II				
Product I Sales to Component II of Major Group 20				
Major Group 20 Component II's *Total* purchase of kindred products	0.001	0.003	0.004	←
Product I Sales to Component II of Major Group 20				
Total Product I sales	1.7	3.3	4.0	
V_{14} — CUSTOMER INDUSTRY III				
Product I Sales to Component III of Major 20 Group				
Major Group 20 Component III's *Total* purchase of kindred products	0.001	0.003	0.002	
Product I Sales to Component III of Major 20 Group				
Total Product I sales	1.1	1.8	1.4	

these sales distributed among the components of the major Industry Group?

Customer Industry I was sold 14.3 percent of the total Product I sales in the year Y_1, and in the next two years, 15.5 and 16.0 percent, respectively. Customer Industry IV purchased 5.7, 5.6, and 5.5 percent of the total sales of Product I in the three years; Customer Industry II — 1.7, 3.3, and 4.0 percent; and Customer Industry III — 1.1, 1.8, and 1.4 percent. *It is these percentages that determine the V-Index for the four Customer Industries,* since they are all components of the Industry Group satisfying the most vital need V_1.

Turning to the importance attached to the purchase of Product I by the industries it serves, we find that more than a fifth of the total *sales* of the product to Industry Group V_1 — food and kindred products — represented only 0.009 percent of the total purchase of products similar to Product I by Standard Classification Major Group 20 — food and kindred products. The next year, the year Y_2, 26.2 percent of the total sales of Product I was made to Major Group 20, but this represented only 0.011 percent of the total purchase of kindred products by the industry. Similarly, in the third years, 26.9 percent of the total sales of Product I represented only 0.013 percent of the total purchases of kindred products by Major Group 20.

Care has to be exercised in arriving at the total purchase of kindred products by Customer Industries. By definition, what we are looking for is the total expenditure on the part of the Customer Industry to obtain products which can be reasonably grouped together with the Product I in want satiability. If we are considering an input used in pasteurizing, homogenizing, vitaminizing, and bottling fluid milk, the expenditure by the Milk Industry for *processing ingredients* would constitute kindred products. Similarly, if we consider *salad oil,* its purchase by Industry 2035 — pickled fruits and vegetables; vegetable sauces and seasonings; salad dressings — must be compared to other products which are used in the manufacture of these products. The idea behind the classification of kindred products is that the relative importance to the Customer Industry is governed, not by the total expenditure on all units by the industry, but only by the expenditure on the segment of this total pertaining to products with comparable want satiability.

Turning again to Table XV, we notice that Major Group 20 – food and kindred products — is an important customer of Product I as far as the organism itself is concerned. However, to Major Group 20 Product I is *not* an important constituent. The absolute percentage figures themselves are extremely low, but the direction indicated by the successive figures is meaningful. Thus, we notice that the percentage that Product I represents in the total purchases of kindred products by Major Group 20 has been increasing over the three years. Since Customer Industry I is a major component of Major Group 20, it is understandable that its corresponding purchase percentages of Product I should also be increasing. Analogous percentages for Customer Industry II are also increasing. However, we notice that purchases by Customer Industry IV, which represents slightly over 5 percent of the total sales of Product I, have been declining. Sales of Product I to Customer Industry III have increased and then decreased during the three-year period under consideration.

What is the story that emerges out of these different measurements? (1) The sales of Product I to *Major Group* 20 — food and kindred products — are an important constituent of the sales of Product I. (2) While the absolute magnitudes of the purchase of Product I by the Major Group 20 are nominal, the relative direction is consistently upward. (3) *Customer Industry I* is the most important constituent of Major Group 20 as far as sales of Product I by the organism are concerned. Since the sales of Product I to Customer Industry I represent two-thirds of the sales to Major Group 20, the possible course of future sales of Product I to Major Group 20 can be gauged from the trend of sales to Customer Industry I. (4) The downward trend of sales of Product I to Customer Industry IV, as well as the vacillation in the sales of Product I to Customer Industry III, are more than offset by the upward trend in Customer Industry I and II purchases of Product I. (5) Significance of sales to other Industry Groups, similar to Major Group 20, has to be determined in order to chart the probable course of Product I sales — particularly because only a little over a fifth of sales is accounted for by the sales of Product I to Major Group 20.

EMPIRICAL ELEMENTS OF S-INDEX

Turning from the empirical elements of V-Index, we examine the four major components which enter into the empirical construction of the S-Index.

In Table XVI, the four major parts of satiability are: (a) Satiability of *Total* Product P, (b) Satiability of Total *Substitute* Product SP, (c) Significance to organism of total product sales, and (d) Satiability of partial product sales to major customers.

How successful has Product P been in satisfying customer wants during the five-year period for which data are available? The price elasticity of demand for Product P for pairs of successive years demonstrates a peculiar feature. *The sign is positive.* It means that if price increases, so will the demand; if price decreases, so will the demand! Three out of four price-

ILLUSTRATIVE EMPIRICAL ELEMENTS OF S-INDEX

Time →

Satiability Measure and Significance	Y_0	Y_1	Y_2	Y_3	Y_4	Y_4/Y_0
A. Satiability of total Product P sales to all customers						
Quantity (Units)	60,684	55,296	79,509	72,570	74,691	
Dollars (1000)	15,323	16,980	22,640	18,350	18,870	
Price elasticity		+1.39	+10.35	+0.56	−0.57	
Percent of growth, quantity	91.7	143.7	91.2	102.8		123.5
Stage of growth						G_2
C. Significance to organism of total product sales						
Percent of organismic sales		13.5	13.5	12.80	12.67	
Weighted percent of sales		12.4	19.4	11.7	12.3	

Satiability Measure and Significance	Y_0	Y_1	Y_2	Y_3	Y_4	Y_4/Y_0
B. Satiability of total substitute Product SP sales to all customers						
Quantity (units)	32,554	30,046	39,826	26,857	30,809	
Cross-elasticity		+1.20	−7.70	+2.08	+2.86	
Percent of growth, maturity	90.0	132.7	67.3	114.5		94.8
Stage of growth						G_3
D. 1. Satiability of partial product sales to major customer I						
Percent of total product sales		37.4	26.7	26.4		
Percent of total customer purchase						
Percent of product growth			92.1	92.3		
Stage of growth						G_3
D. 2. Satiability of partial product sales to major customer II						
Percent of total product sales		14.5	11.0	8.3		
Percent of total customer purchase						
Percent of product growth			100.7	92.2		
Stage of growth						G_3

elasticity values have the positive sign; so also the cross-elasticity values for the Substitute Product. Turning to the *magnitude* we find that total sales of Product P are generally responsive to changes in price; but the demand for the Substitute Product SP is more than *twice* as responsive to the changes in price of Product P.

The total quantity of Product P sold in the fifth year, Y_4, was higher by 23.5 percent over the first year, Y_0, while that of the Substitute Product SP decreased by 5.2 percent. As a summary measure of the information presented in Part A, Product P could be considered to be in stage G_2 and the Substitute Product in stage G_3.

What are the prospects for Product P sales? We find that the purchase by Major Customer I of Product P is in stage G_3. The sales to Major Customer I represent about a third of the total sales of Product P. Therefore, the stage of the product sales to Major Customer I, G_3, is significant. Going down the line, and investigating the purchase of Product P by Major Customer II, we find that it has represented about a seventh of the total sales of Product P. The stage of growth of sales to Major Customer II also is G_3. With major customers representing a third to a half of the total sales in G_3, prospects for the growth of Product P sales in the near future do not appear to be bright.

What has been the *significance to the organism* of the total product sales? We find that the dollar value of the sales of Product P represented about 13 percent of the total sales revenue of the organism. It probably means that the product is one of the seven or eight major contributors to the total revenue of the organism; it definitely means that the contribution of Product P to the organism is approximately one-eighth to one-seventh of the total sales. In order to make the comparative percentages of contribution to organismic sales by different products comparable, we may want to weight the percentage of the product sales in the total by its rate of growth.

Thus, in the year Y_1, Product P sales were 91.7 percent of the sales in the year Y_0. Multiplying the 13.5 percent that Product P sales contributed to the total sales of the organism in year Y_1, by the rate of growth between the periods Y_0 and Y_1, 13.5×91.7 percent, we obtain the weighted percentage of growth as 12.4 percent. Similarly, weighting the 13.5 percent fraction for the year Y_2 by the growth between years Y_1 and Y_2, 143.7 percent, we obtain a weighted percentage of sales of 19.4 percent. Similarly, for the years Y_3 and Y_4 we have the weighted percentage of growth, respectively, of 11.7 and 12.3 percent. The "raw" percentage of Product P sales for Y_3 and Y_4 are quite close: 12.80 and 12.67 percent. However, since 12.80 percent was the fraction of the total organismic sales in a year when the growth was 91.2 percent, and since 12.67 percent was the fraction of the total organismic sales in a year which had a growth of 102.8 percent, the *lower* figure represents a *higher* weighted percentage of sales in the total picture. The purpose of the weighting is to incorporate into the absolute sales figures an appropriate growth factor, so that the contribution of the particular product(s) may be given recognition with respect to not only its *absolute sales*, but also its *stage of growth*.

We see in Table XVII that Product I sales to Customer Industry II grew 141.0 percent between years Y_1 and Y_2. The sales in year Y_2 represented 3.0 percent of the total organism's sales. Product I sales to Customer Industry III grew 125.0 percent between years Y_1 and Y_2. The Product I sales to Customer Industry III represented 1 percent of the total organismic sales in Y_2. The growth of Product I sales to Customer Industry IV was 142.5 percent and its share of organismic sales 0.2 percent. The weighted growth of three segments of Product I are respectively: 4.2, 1.3, and 0.3 percent. The weighted sales of the three segments of Product I sales by stage G_2 is the *sum* of these weighted percentages of growth of the Product I sales to Customer Industries II, III, and IV, the sales to which of Product I are in the rapid growth stage, G_2.

We also find that Product I sales to Customer I *declined* between years Y_1 and Y_2, the rate of growth being 93.0 percent. In the year Y_2, the Product I sales to Customer Industry I represented 5.4 percent of the total

TABLE XVII

PRODUCT'S SATIABILITY
ILLUSTRATIVE EMPIRICAL SITUATION:

(1) Product I Sales to Customer Industries

Growth Stage	Sales Segment	Growth Rate, Percent	Percent Share of Organismic Sales	Weighted Sales Percent of Segments by Growth
	Product I sales to:			
	Customer Industry II	141.0	3.0	4.2
Stage G_2	Customer Industry III	125.0	1.0	1.3
	Customer Industry IV	142.5	0.2	0.3
	Weighted growth rate by stage G_2			5.8
	Product I sales to:			
Stage G_3	Customer Industry I	93.0	5.4	5.0
	Weighted growth rate by stage G_3			5.0

sales of the organism: which, when weighted by the growth rate of the Product I sales to Customer Industry I, becomes 5.0 percent.

In this illustrative empirical situation, we find that Product I sales to Customer Industries II, III, and IV are in the stage of rapid growth, and Product I sales to Customer Industry I are in the maturation stage. If these were the only customers for Product I sales, we find that the weighted growth rate in the rapid growth is almost nearly equaled by that in maturation.

Turning from the *sales segments of a product,* to *different products* which can satisfy the wants of the outside world, we find in Table XVIII the satiability of six products of the organism. We find that Product I is in stage G_2: there are other customers, outside of Customer Industries I, II, III, and IV the sales to which are a standoff in growth. The total sales of Product I represent 19.0 percent of the total sales of the organism. The Product II sales amount to 0.2 percent of the organism's sales, Product III 3.6 percent, Product IV 4.3 percent, Product V 0.8 percent, and Product VI, 26.1 percent. It should be noted that the total fraction of the organismic sales

TABLE XVIII

PRODUCT'S SATIABILITY

ILLUSTRATIVE EMPIRICAL SITUATION:

(2) Product I, II, III, IV, V, VI Sales

Growth Stage	Products	Growth Rate, Percent	Percent Share of Organismic Sales	Weighted Growth By Product
Stage G_1	Product II	67.6	0.2	0.1
	Weighted growth rate by stage G_1			0.1
Stage G_2	Product I	113.5	19.0	21.6
	Product III	137.6	3.6	4.9
	Product IV	200.8	4.3	8.6
	Weighted growth rate by stage G_2			35.1
Stage G_3	Product VI	115.3	26.1	30.1
	Weighted growth rate by stage G_3			30.1
Stage G_4	Product V	91.1	0.8	0.7
	Weighted growth rate by stage G_4			0.7
	Total		54.0	66.0

represented by the sales of these six products is *not 100 percent, but only 54 percent.* In fact, these six products constitute a Product Group of the organism. When the respective contributions of the products to the total organismic sales are weighted by the respective growth percentages, we find that the products representing 54 percent of the total sales is equivalent to 66.0 percent of weighted sales.

The assignment of stages of growth is not made solely on the growth rate in the years Y_1 and Y_2. There were previous instances of data available based on which growth curves were computed to arrive at the appropriate growth stages.

Kinetics of Death

The weighted growth rates in the different stages can in fact exceed 100 percent. In fact, if the organism is to grow, the forces of growth should exceed those of death. In terms of life-cycle terminology, weighted growth rates in G_1 and G_2 should exceed those in G_3 and G_4. If weighted growth rates in G_1 and G_2 add to say 50 percent and those in G_3 and G_4 to 51 percent, the organism is "dead." If it were reversed, it is gasping but alive; should the sum of the weighted growth rates in G_1 and G_2 be significantly higher than those in G_3 and G_4, then the organism is alive and kicking.

An appropriate measure of organismic growth would thus be the ratio

$$\frac{\text{Sum of weighted growth rates in } G_1 \text{ and } G_2}{\text{Sum of weighted growth rates in } G_3 \text{ and } G_4}$$

This ratio should be *statistically significantly* greater than 1 for the healthy survival of the organism.

Reference was made earlier to the role of the different stages of growth in the life cycle of the product, characterized as "fat" and "lean" years. Stages G_1 and G_2 could be considered "fat" years, and G_3 and G_4 "lean" years. Provision has to be made in the stages of "fat" years in order to counteract the tendencies toward death and decay in the subsequent stages of "lean" years.

> Death occurs when the rate at which an organism does work to restore the original state is less than that demanded to overcome the effects of a given challenge. . . .
> The magnitudes of challenges (or, more appropriately, the responses required to overcome these challenges) are distributed energetically like a Maxwell-Boltzmann distribution of energies among molecules. . . .

> A theory of kinetics of death is presented which is based upon the experimentally determined Gompertz function and the two following postulates: (1) The distribution of stress magnitudes is a Maxwell-Boltzmann distribution; (2) An organism dies when stress magnitude exceeds the organism's maximum ability to compensate therefor.[9]

The stochastic model which relates observations on aging, physiologic decline, mortality, and radiation, referred to in the quotation above has successfully claimed a great deal of correspondence with independent observations. An agreement between prediction and observation does not "prove" the validity of the model, as the authors readily agree. Their theory is expressed in terms of energy fluctutations arising internally or externally. Their reasons for choice of this dimensional system are:

> (1) Death undoubtedly cannot occur without the occurrence of a change in structure or physiological state, which change is the result of energy expenditure; (2) death will occur if the capacity of the system to restore conditions necessary for life is exceeded; (3) This restoration of original conditions requires the expenditure of energy of a certain kind at a certain minimum rate. Thus, an organism lives or dies according to whether its maximum power output in the challenged modality is sufficient to overcome the disruptive influence of the challenge.[10]

This theory, which has been advanced and tested with a considerable degree of success in predicting behavior in human beings, is significant from the point of view of the life-cycle theory of products. Of particular interest is the concept of death as the occurrence of a change in the structure of physiological state when the capacity of the system to restore conditions necessary for life is exceeded. There is a direct parallel in the relationship between weighted growth rates by stage of the organism. In Table XVII, the weighted growth rate in stage G_2, 5.8 percent, is almost completely balanced by the weighted growth rate in stage G_3 of 5 percent. If the weighted growth rates were reversed, and G_3 stage had 5.8 percent and G_2 had only 5.0 percent, "death" would occur, with the consequence that the total of Product I sales to Customer Industries I, II, III, and IV would decline. Similarly, in Table XVIII, we find that the weighted growth rate by stages G_1 and G_2, 35.2 percent, has a slight edge over the weighted growth rate by stages G_3 and G_4, 30.8 percent. Here again, if the situations were

---

[9] Bernard L. Strehler and Albert S. Mildvan, "General Theory of Mortality and Aging," *Science,* vol. 132 (July 1, 1963), pp. 15, 20.

[10] *Ibid.,* p. 21n.

reversed, it would mean "death" for the organism insofar as the performance of the Product Group consisting of Products I–VI were concerned.

It is significant to note that the theory of kinetics of death is based,
in part, upon the experimentally determined Gompertz function. It will be
recalled that the National Industrial Conference Board based its study of
growth patterns in over 30 industries in agriculture, fuels, metals, nonmetals, transportation, and other fields using the Gompertz curve of a
similar form.

LIFE CYCLE OF PRODUCTS

In Figure 20 the weighted growth rate percentages by stage are

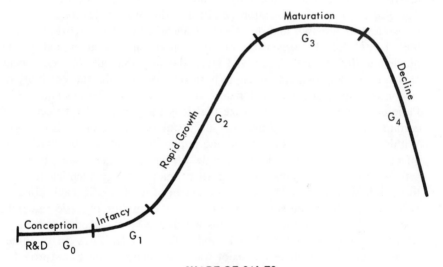

SHARE OF SALES

Stage G_1 0.1%
Stage G_2 35.1%
Stage G_3 30.1%
Stage G_4 0.7%

IN THE EMPIRICAL SITUATION:

1. G_2 & G_3 predominate.
2. Product entering G_3 should have <u>ready</u> replacement from R&D
3. Product entering G_4 should have <u>immediate</u> replacement from R&D.
4. Allowing for time lag R&D replacement program should have started
   X years ago.

Figure 20. PRODUCT LIFE CYCLE — EMPIRICAL ILLUSTRATION.

shown in diagramatic form. In the empirical situation, G_2 and G_3 predominate. When a product enters G_3, it should have its replacement from research and development *ready*; while a product entering G_4 should have *immediate* replacement from research and development. Since the research and development process takes time, the replacement for the products entering stages G_3 and G_4 should be initiated sufficiently early, allowing for the time lag.

PERIODIC TABLE OF PRODUCT DIVERSIFICATION

We present in Table XIX the Periodic Table of Product Diversification. The different elements constituting the Table have been discussed at length, and empirically illustrated. The great usefulness of the Periodic Table of Product Diversification (PTPD) is that it provides for *preventive* investment in research and development ahead of time in such a way that the "death" of the organism, or its components, is attempted to be prevented. Its strength is derived from the fact that all the component elements are empirical and relate to both sides of the coin, the satiability of customer wants, and the vital nature of the wants of the customer. The Periodic Table seeks to emphasize that it is the successful satisfaction of certain wants that will ensure the successful operation of the organism. Within this framework, both basic and applied research can be considered effectively. The nature and magnitude of the customer wants that are satisfied by applied research are perhaps more readily identifiable than those of basic research. The only requirement of the Periodic Table concept is that there should be some customers for the outputs of basic research, and that they should have some wants which can be classified according to their respective intensities. The Periodic Table underscores an often-neglected fact of alternative sources of want satisfaction, sometimes provided by the same organism in competition with some other outputs of its own. Should there be a perceptible movement towards the substitute products, the organism may detect it early and foster such shift in demand to its own advantage.

Provision is made in the Periodic Table composition for the identification of stages of growth of products, whether manually or by means of a computer program. Such identification can be compared with the empirical results obtained for the respective industries as a whole, of which certain outputs (products) of the organism are a part. This contextual framework for the stages of growth would provide meaningful aids for constructing an index to highlight the state-of-the-organism itself. An aggregate index of some sort for the organism as a whole should reflect

not only the present earnings, but also potentialities of the organism for future earnings.

Thus, even as Mendeléyev's periodic table indicated, by its very structure, missing elements, so also the Periodic Table of Product Diversification is proposed as a systematic means for a continuing review of an organism's output portfolio. An output is intended to satisfy at least one want, and its ability to satisfy the want, its *S-Index* (page 129), is evaluated by the consumer in terms of the vital nature of the want satisfied, its *V-Index*. Within the framework of the PTPD, the elements of strength and weakness of the component markets of each output are highlighted, as well as the stage of its growth, so that: (1) the predominant sales performance of a few groups in favorable growth stages does not give the impression of innate strength of the *entire* output portfolio, and (2) advantage can be taken of the groundwork laid in the V-Index by Output 1 to introduce another, a complementary Product 2. The (a) types of products which need be introduced (b) at specific periods of time in the future (c) to take the place of other products expected to decline by that time, read from the PTPD, constitute readily understandable information to management for effective allocation of corporate resources.

Quid enim varietas moblitasque casuam perturbabit,
si certus sis adversus incerta? [For what disturbances can
result from the changes and instability of Chance, if you
are sure in the face of that which is unsure?]

SENECA, *Epistulae ad Lucilium*, ci, 9

Right notions are based on (a) right perception, (b)
right inference, and (c) right testimony.

PATANJALI, *Yoga-sūtras* 1.6

That intelligence which is found to be embodied in
modified forms of the nonintelligent elements is produced in the same way in which the red color is
produced from the combination of betel, areca nut, and
lime.

SARVEPALLI RADHAKRISHNAN, "Cārvāka," in
SARVEPALLI RADHAKRISHNAN and CHARLES A. MOORE, (eds.),
A Source Book in Indian Philosophy
(Princeton, N. J.: Princeton University Press, 1957) p. 227

CHAPTER SIX

CENTRAL INTELLIGENCE RETRIEVAL SYSTEM

While the integrated picture emerging from PTPD (Periodic Table of Product Diversification) provides a fruitful framework to derive intelligence out of the information from within the organism, in the competitive context of profit-making enterprises in a free-enterprise system, there is a need to generate intelligence about competitive activity, present and potential.

Such intelligence needs by no means be designed to be used competitively; in fact, considerable use can be made of it to mutual advantage.

In either event, the effort is to counteract the "disturbances that can result from changes and instability of Chance." Although it would hardly make one immune to the disturbances, it can contribute to one's being "sure

157

in the face of that which is unsure." To be forewarned is to be forearmed.

The armor against uncertainty will be as dependable as the elements it is made of: their individual strengths and weaknesses, their collective strengths and weaknesses, and the warrantability of the construction of the armor from the constituent elements. Therefore, in constructing an armor of intelligence out of the elements of information, "right perception," and "right testimony" are invaluable features of the information and "right inference" is an indispensable feature of the intelligence generation.

The output of intelligence is more than the input of the different pieces of information. It is neither the sum nor the product of the different pieces, but a harmonizing of the pieces in such a way that they are blended together. The betel leaf that Radhakrishnan refers to in the quotation above, is green, areca nut brown, and lime white; but when they are chewed together, as is done in the East, they blend to produce a reddish color.

We followed the progress of a technically feasible idea through the series of management decisions to its output stage in Chapters 3 and 4. In the preceding chapter we discussed the processing of current information of the performance of the output to anticipate potential outputs.

Physical products are not the only outputs, although it is easier to visualize manufacturing a physical product and marketing it. Ideas are certainly outputs; and the innovations of systems and their invention are certainly outputs whether or not any hardware or physical product is associated with them.

Ideas industries account for an increasing share of the Gross National Product. It is said that as time goes on, agricultural outputs may be contributing approximately 5 percent of GNP, and industrial outputs involving physical products another 15 or 20 percent, leaving as much as 75 percent of GNP to be made up of outputs not involving physical products. Information of one type or other may be generated, communicated, evaluated, and acted upon; the activity involving ideas making up the major activity contributing to GNP.

Turning from the national context to that of the individual organism itself, we may consider the almost inevitable generation of ideas along with physical outputs. Before the organism manufactures the physical product, it should know how to manufacture it, and if the process of such manufacture is developed internally, there are questions of establishing the legal claim to the process or processes which have to be faced long before the decisions about the physical manufacture. In other words, the investment in R&D raises the questions of the disposition of the ideas generated by the investment even before the questions of the disposition of whatever physical products may be associated with the ideas.

The intelligence about competitive activity, both present and potential, generated via a Central Intelligence Retrieval System (CIRS) would complement the intelligence of the organism's own performance reflected in the Periodic Table of Product Diversification; and the aid to decision-making offered by CIRS with reference to the output of ideas would complement the aid to decision-making offered by PTPD with reference to the output of physical products.

IDENTIFICATION OF PATENT ACQUISITIONS

TO PATENT OR NOT TO PATENT

One measure of the core of technical advances, whether of the nation or of an enterprise, is the number of the different types of patents accrued to its credit. Under the Constitution, the Congress has power "to promote the Progress of Science and useful Arts, by securing for limited Times to Authors and Inventors the exclusive Right to their respective Writings and Discoveries." (Art. 1, Sect. 8.) Since patents have thus been recognized as a means "to promote the Progress of Science and useful Arts," it is only reasonable to consider the quantity of patents as an acceptable measure of the progress of science and arts, the quality of the patents being an obvious complement to the criterion of their quantity.

> The countries which issue the most patents are the United States, Germany, France, Great Britain, Italy, Canada, Belgium, Switzerland, Japan, Australia, Spain and Sweden, in approximately the order named. The numbers issued by these countries vary from year to year and the rank of some would shift, but the number of 40,000 for the highest and 4,000 for the lowest of the countries named gives a general idea of the range.[1]

An obvious omission is the U.S.S.R. Presumably the reason for the omission would be the fact that the U.S.S.R. is not a signatory to the International Convention for the Protection of Industrial Property.

Turning from the international and national activity in patents to the process of acquisition and disposition of patents by individual enterprises, the first question is: to patent or not to patent.

The investment made by the organism in R&D generally yields technical advancements of varying degree and kind, some of which may well qualify under the criterion of novelty, making them eligible for the

---

[1] J. Frederico Pasquale, "Patents — International," *Encyclopaedia Britannica* (Chicago: 1960), vol. 17, p. 372.

issuance of a patent. Should the organism proceed to obtain the patent or not?

It is true that for the explicit use of the specific process, the patent-owner has to be compensated by patent-users. However, if the patent itself indicates a vital stage in the development of a larger process being investigated by a competitor, the organism's patent may be used as an input to yield an output which would make it unnecessary for the competitor to depend on the legal rights of the organism for the particular patent. Further, the disclosure of the very fact that the organism is working in a particular field may be imparting more information to the competitors than is warranted by the establishment of the legal rights to the particular patent by the organism.

To patent or not to patent is essentially a question of evaluating the future in the present. Even after the decision has been made to patent a particular technological advancement that has accrued to the organism, two major questions remain: (1) to use or not to use the patent; and (2) to license or not to license. The first question relates to the profitability to the organism in using its own technical know-how to manufacture output. If it were more profitable to let someone else manufacture, using the patent for a fee, than for the organism itself to undertake the manufacture, then the question would become one of profitable licensing, which consists of finding the right licensee at the right time.

TO LICENSE OR NOT TO LICENSE

Several uncertainties of a serious nature enter into the picture of patent licensing. By making available to a customer the technical knowledge in the exclusive possession of the organism, care has to be exercised to make sure that this would not impair the capabilities for output of the organism — either present or potential. If the organism is already manufac-turing an output, using the technology of a more powerful patent than that offered for licensing, the problem is relatively simple. If, however, it were to license a patent *today* in an area of endeavor not entered by the organism, and if that licensing has to be based on guesses about possible lines of output *tomorrow,* then the guess is at best a hazardous one.

In order to determine whether or not a particular output would be of interest to the organism in the future, it is essential to have a reasonable system of prediction of the direction of the output of the organism. This requires the laying down of a strategy of output development for a sufficiently long period in the future. Once you have a list of outputs, both present and potential, it can be checked against the available patents at the disposition of the organism. This comparison would indicate how much of the know-how accrued to the organism represents present and potential interest for the outputs of the organism itself. If it is likely that the know-how would be of consequence to a development project some time in the future, it may be advisable to reserve the use of the patent for the organism itself.

However, this is an "iffy" proposition. There is little guarantee that the contemplated outputs by the organism will in fact be the actual products undertaken tomorrow, because the profile of output tomorrow is a *guess* made today on the basis of existing technology and expectations of technological breakthroughs. Such guesswork can be fortified by asking people in the know about aspects of future patent utilization. For instance, the inventor of a patent is quite likely to have some ideas as to the potential uses of his invention. The market-intelligence personnel will have some clues as to the future output plans of similar organisms in the field. The sales data of the organism may disclose a shift in demand pattern of some of the customers, which may lead to an indirect suggestion about outputs by other organisms.

Influencing significantly the profile of future products of an organism is the output strategy of other organisms satisfying similar needs of customers. Similar to the expectations of technological breakthroughs which were discussed earlier, there are *expectations of outputs by other organisms,* which would effectively condition the reserve of patent knowledge that the organism may wish to keep for contingent use in the future. In order to be effective, the organism needs not only information about its own future profile of output, but also the expected profiles of output of other organisms. It is hard enough to guess what one might find profitable to manufacture tomorrow; it is much more hazardous to venture a guess as to what one's competitors will undertake in the future. Nevertheless, this has to be done — and it is being done, by design or by default. On the basis of these guesses, a large or small segment of the organism's inventions is used currently, a similar segment reserved for possible future use, and the remainder set apart for licensing.

AN ELECTRONIC PATENTS FILE?

The backlog of scores of patents decided not to be used by the manufacturer in the forseeable future, and an increasing accumulation of new patents, a majority of which were similarly designated for nonuse by the manufacturer, led to the request for operations research assistance. The problem was stated in the following terms: (i) A very large number of patents which would not be used by the manufacturer had accumulated over the period of years; (ii) requests for the licensing of many of these patents came to the manufacturer from potential customers who had received word, either through announcement in technical literature or in the patent literature; (iii) such requests could not be readily or adequately processed because the information relating to the patents was not available in any organized form; (iv) only a small fraction of the new patents accruing to the manufacturer would be used in its own manufacturing process; (v) the rate of new accruals of patents had increased in the recent years; (vi) therefore, the prospects were for an even larger accumulation of unused patents, which were not only unused but also designated for nonuse by the manufacturer for the forseeable future; (vii) the contribution of a "novel" nature to the existing body of knowledge has to be established before a patent issues; the more technologically advanced the discipline, the more excruciating the detailed level at which such a contribution can be established — as in, say, the distinction between a patent involving alkyl alkylphosphono*tri*thioates and another involving alkyl alkylphosphono*di*thioates; hence any useful record of patents has as an essential prerequisite an effective and consistent system of detailed classification of relevant concepts; (viii) was there in existence, or could there be evolved, an adequate filing system — preferably electronic — which would furnish a source of ready access and retrieval of the desired patents as the requests for the licensing of them came along?

Thus, the "client" asked for an electronic file of patents. Diagnostic probing started out in the area of ultimate use of the electronic file when established. What would the "client" do with the information that patent number 2,345,678 was related, say, to a curing process for salmon and pork? After all, this information was already available in the U.S. Patent Sheet 2,345,678. If a customer interested in the curing of salmon were to ask for licensing of *that specific patent,* then there would be little problem, and consequently little contribution by the mere transfer from an 8½ by 11 sheet to an 80-column punch card. However, if the question was: "What patents do you have available for licensing in the area of curing, whether of salmon, or fish in general; and of pork, or meat in general?" then the coded information would be useful in facilitating a search for all the entries under "curing."

It turned out that the desire of the "client" was not merely to be a *passive* respondent to the requests that originate on the outside and come searching for patents in the possession of the manufacturer, but to *actively* pursue customers — present, as well as potential. *In other words, the diagnostic probing resulted in a totally fresh statement of the problem, converting it from a request for an electronic file of patents to a system which answers the question*: Given a patent, who are likely to be interested in it?; and, given a customer — present or potential — what are all the patents in the possession of the manufacturer which may be of interest to the customer?

CLASSIFICATION OF PATENT NOVELTY INFORMATION: CONTENTS AND CUSTOMERS

The operations-research approach to the problem highlighted the need for an effective means of integrating the information about both patents and their potential users. This information existed in bits and pieces in departments of the organism. When integrated, the information inputs would aid in the disbursement of current technical know-how, represented by the patents, more by design and less by default. As a corollary, it was found that the system of integration of information, undertaken in the interest of patent licensing, paved the way for an *overall flow of information* between the departments of the company through a central medium.

The major elements in this system of intelligence retrieval were: (i) patent information, and (ii) customer information. *By intelligence retrieval is meant the programmed activity which would permit the emergence of a connected story about a patent or a customer or a patent-customer relationship, by the prearranged, skillful juxtaposition of apparently unrelated bits of information contributed by different departments of the company.*

(A) CONTENT: 1. STANDARD INDUSTRIAL CLASSIFICATION SYSTEM (SIC)

The Intelligence Retrieval System had as its cornerstone the Standard Industrial Classification (SIC) of the United States Government. The SIC hierarchy from "Division" through "Industry" was discussed on pages 135-136. However, in order to effectively plan for the future of outputs by the organism, the SIC hierarchy through Industry was found to be inadequate. A patent may be potentially useful in the meat-packing industry. But in what part of the meat-packing industry is this likely to be used? Meat-packing plants include: establishment primarily engaged in the slaughtering, for their own account or on a contract basis for the trade, of cattle, hogs, sheep, lambs, calves, horses, and other animals, except small game, for meat to be sold or to be used on the same premises in canning or curing, and in making sausage, lard, and other products. In which of the hundreds of processes involved in the activity of the meat-packing plants establishment is the patent useful — now or in the future? Is it for the slaughtering of cattle, or for the slaughtering of hogs, or of sheep, or of lambs, or of calves, or of horses, or of other animals? Is it likely to be useful in canning or curing? Or in making sausage, lard, or other products? Thus, to know merely that a patent is potentially useful in the meat-packing industry is of little help to the possessor of the patent in deciding whether or not to hold on to the patent or to license it out to some other organism.

Two further subdivisions of "Industry" in the SIC (Standard Industrial Classification) were found to be helpful. The first one is the *Product Group;* and the second one is the *Product Code.* The Industry Number carries the division classification to four digits; the Product Group to the fifth digit; and the Product Code to the seventh digit. The Product Groups which are subdivisions of the Industry 2011, meat packing plant products, are: 20111 — fresh beef, 20112 — fresh veal, 20113 — fresh lamb and mutton, 20114 — fresh pork, 20116 — hides, skins, and pelts, and 20117 — other meat-packing-plant products, not elsewhere classified.

These five-digit Product Groups themselves are further broken down into seven-digit Product Codes. Thus, under 20111 (fresh beef) we find the Products 2011111 — fresh and frozen (beef), including carcass, primal cuts, boneless, etc., and 2011151 — fresh and frozen variety meats (edible organs: heart, liver, brains, kidneys, etc.). Under the Product Code 20112 — fresh veal — we find Product 2011211 — fresh and frozen (veal), including carcass, primal cuts, boneless, etc., hide-off basis; and Product 2011251 — fresh and frozen variety meats (edible organs: heart, liver, brains, kidneys, etc.), and so on.

Reference was made to a hypothetical patent relating to a curing process. If such a patent were available, the potential customer for it could be sought in the subdivision of Industry Group 20 — Food and kindred products or Industry 2013 — sausages and other prepared meat products. These consist of "establishments primarily engaged in manufacturing sausages, cured meats, smoked meats, canned meats, frozen meats, other prepared meats, and meat specialties, from purchased carcasses and other materials. Sausage kitchens and other prepared-meat plants operated by packing houses as separate establishments are also included in this industry."[2] The patent for curing meat may be potentially useful in one or more of the several Product Codes which are components of Industry 2013. For instance, Product 2013111 — sweet pickled or dry cured pork —

---

[2] Executive Office of the President, Bureau of the Budget, *Standard Industrial Classification Manual* (Washington, D.C.: U.S. Government Printing Office, 1957), p. 47.

seems to be a good choice for a first try. According to the Census of Manufactures, conducted in 1954, we find that 677,465,000 pounds of sweet pickled or dry cured pork were shipped in 1954, representing a value of $286,428,000.[3] The Product Group 2013600 — other processed pork, not specified by kind, may also be a potential customer for the patent for curing meat. The value of the shipments of Product 2013600 was $78,251,000[4] in 1963 compared with $57,435,000 in 1958 and $54,126,000 in 1954.

It is evident that, had we used the hierarchy of Standard Industrial Classification only through the Minor Group level, we would have gone no further than 201 — meat-products establishments. When we went one level below, we identified Industry 2013 — sausages and other prepared meat-products establishments. At the Product Group level, we were able to identify Product Group 20131 — pork, processed and cured. By proceeding to the next hierarchy of classification, we identified Product 2013111 — sweet pickled or dry cured pork and Product 2013100 — other processed pork, not identified by kind. This hierarchy is represented in Figure 21.

This progressive investigation down the line of Standard Industrial Classification also suggests that we may try other *Products* within the Product Group 20131, as well as 2013111 and 2013100. In addition, other Product Groups may be tried: for instance, Product Group 20132 — sausage and other prepared meat products, not canned, represented a total shipment value of $1,274,671,000 in 1954, $1,526,214,000 in 1958 and $1,733,710,000 in 1963. Product Group 20134 — dried beef and other cured meats, represented a shipment value of $90,994,000 in 1954. This Product Group has two subdivisions of particular interest to the patent for meat curing: Product 2013411 — pickled or cured (except dried and dehydrated) beef, of which 90,985,000 pounds were shipped in 1954, at a value of $42,687,000; and Product 2013400 — dried beef and other cured meats, not specified by kind, of which there was a shipment worth $4,002,000 in 1954. In 1963 these items are included in Product 2011171 — other edible beef including corn beef, and had a shipment value of $46,612,000.

The term "product" as used in the Census of Manufactures, represents the *finest level of detail* for which output information

[3] 1954 *Census of Manufacturers, Vol. II; Industry Statistics, Part I: General Summary and Major* Groups 20 – 28 (Washington, D. C.: U.S. Government Printing Office, 1957), pp. 20A – 12ff.

[4] 1963 *Census of Manufacturers, Vol. II; Industry Statistics, Part I: General Summary and Major Groups* 20 – 28 (Washington, D. C.: U.S. Government Printing Office, 1966), in press.

DIVISION D: MANUFACTURING

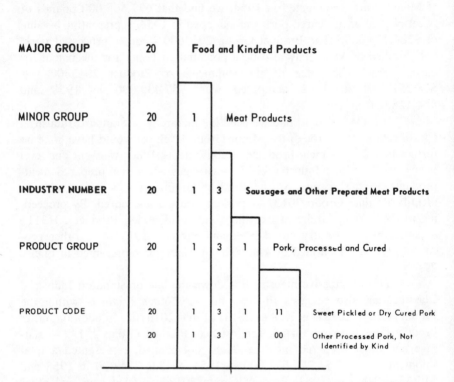

Figure 21. UNITED STATES STANDARD INDUSTRIAL CLASSIFICATION (SIC SYSTEM).

was requested. Consequently, it is not necessarily synonymous with the term "product" as used in the marketing sense. For example, all grades of automotive gasoline were reported as a single item. On the other hand, cotton broad-woven goods were distributed into nearly 200 items. (Italics supplied.)

The list of products for which separate information was collected in the 1954 Census was based on the product categories selected for the 1947 Census of Manufactures after extensive consultation with industry and government representatives.... For the purpose of summarizing the product information, the separate products were aggregated into "classes of products," which were in turn grouped into all "primary" products of each industry. The code structure used is a 7-digit number for the individual products, a 5-digit code for the class of product, and a 4-digit number code for the total primary products in an industry.

The 7,000 product items in the 1954 census were grouped into approximately 1,000 separate classes on the basis of general similarity of manufacturing processes, types of materials used, and the like. However, the grouping of products was affected by the economic significance of the class, and in some cases, dissimilar products were grouped because they were not sufficiently significant to warrant separate classes. . . .

The Bureau of the Census is prohibited by law from publishing any statistics that disclose information reported by individual companies. In the 1954 census, as in 1947, preference was given to the geographic regions and divisions over individual States in applying disclosure rules; similarly, States took precedence over standard metropolitan areas, while such areas were given preference over counties, and counties, over cities. . . . Such order-of-precedence was used because (1) It was considered preferable to show regional data for an industry, even at the cost of withholding data for another (usually the least important) State in a region, rather than to show all publishable data for the individual States and group the disclosure States throughout the United States in an "all other" category as was done in the 1939 and earlier censuses; and (2) by giving preference to industry group statistics over individual industries within each State, the extent to which individual States can be compared within the S.I.C. industry classification framework is greatly increased.[5]

(A) CONTENT: (2) NEW INDUSTRIES, TITLES, DEFINITIONS

Patents usually relate to novel ways of making, or unmaking, things and services. Therefore, it is quite conceivable that the particular patent for curing fish and meat may not be visualized as yet by the establishments engaged in the manufacture of sweet pickled or dry cured pork, other processed pork not specified by kind, or dried beef and other cured meats, not specified by kind. For all we know, this particular curing process may mark the beginning of a new industry altogether. In order to qualify for a "line" in the *Census of Manufactures,* the minimum requirement is approximately 5,000,000 units or $5,000,000 worth of sales of the particular product in the year of the Census of Manufactures. The use of the patent for curing may give an exceptional advantage to its early user in the particular segment of the processing industry, long before the industry merits a "line" in the *Census.*

Provision is made for changes and additions as is warranted by the experience gained in the use of SIC, supplements to which are issued from time to time.

---

[5] 1954 *Census of Manufacturers, Vol. II; Industry Statistics, Part I: General Summary and Major Groups* 20 – 28 (Washington, D.C.: U.S. Government Printing Office, 1957), pp. XX, XXIV.

The 1963 Supplement contains new industries, titles, and definitions; amendments in titles, definitions, and index items; industries combined, reconstituted, or deleted; coding interpretation; and additional index items. It embodies the results of the experience of government agencies in using the 1957 Standard Industrial Classification for five years. It also reflects, insofar as limitations of review procedures for the 1962 evaluation permit, technological advancement, and expansion and contraction of industries. . . .

Since the 1962 review of the Standard Industrial Classification was primarily an evaluation of industries (four digits) in terms of data from the 1958 economic censuses, review procedures prohibited changes in major groups (two digits) and groups (three digits). This limited changes to those affecting only industries (four digits) within single groups (three digits).[6]

In the Major Group 20 — food and kindred products, we notice that there are two definitions for new industries. (1) Industry 2095 — roasted coffee establishments primarily engaged in roasting coffee, and in manufacturing coffee concentrates and extracts in powdered, liquid, or frozen form (previously part of Industry 2099). Industry 2099 comprises establishments primarily engaged in manufacturing prepared foods and miscellaneous food specialties, not elsewhere classified, such as baking powder, yeast, and other leavening compounds, roasted coffee and coffee extracts. We notice that roasted coffee has graduated from this miscellaneous class to merit a line of its own. (2) the Industries 2049 — grease and tallow, and 2095 — animal and marine fats and oils, except grease and tallow, were combined into a new Industry 2049 — animal and marine fats and oils, including grease and tallow.

While no earth-shaking changes were taking place in Major Group 20 — food and kindred products, Group 19 — ordnance and accessories, was subject to some major changes. In the 1957 SIC Manual, guided missiles and space vehicles were not listed separately, but were submerged under the "miscellaneous" category, Industry 1929 — ammunition, not elsewhere classified. It comprised of establishments primarily engaged in manufacturing ammunition, not elsewhere classified, including bombs, mines, torpedoes, grenades, depth charges, chemical warfare projectiles, and their component parts — no mention of guided missiles anywhere. The 1963 *Supplement to the* 1957 *Edition (of the) SIC Manual* defines a new Industry 1925 — guided missiles and space vehicles, completely assembled.

---

6 The Executive Office of the President, Bureau of the Budget, *Supplement to the 1957 Edition Standard Industrial Classification Manual,* (Washington, D.C.: U.S. Government Printing Office, 1963), p. 3.

Under this group come establishments primarily engaged in manufacturing completely assembled guided missiles and space vehicles. Establishments primarily engaged in manufacturing guided-missile and space-vehicle engines and engine parts are classified in Industry 3722 — aircraft engines and engine parts. Space satellites, guided missile and space-vehicle airborne and ground guidance, checkout and launch electronic systems and components are grouped in Industry 3662 — radio and television transmitting, signaling, and detection equipment and apparatus. Guided-missile and space-vehicle airframes, nose cones, and space capsules are grouped in Industry 3729 — aircraft parts and auxiliary equipment, not elsewhere classified.

Although the responsiveness of the Standard Industrial Classification system to the thrusts in technology is governed via the number of units of value of the output using these thrusts in technology, the SIC system provides the most comprehensive classification of its kind available in the United States. It is not only comprehensive, but is also flexible. Manufacturing and other industries are required by law to file statistics relating to their operations within the framework of the Standard Industrial Classification. It behooves the organism to take advantage of the wealth of information provided by the Census of Manufactures, using the Standard Industrial Classification system. Since any and every economic activity in the United States is classified under one or the other of the classes of the SIC, every present and potential user of the patent in the possession of the organism can be identified within the SIC framework. In many instances, it may be found to be inadequate; however, its value as an excellent starting point is undeniable.

(A) CONTENT: (3) TECHNOMETRIC STRUCTURE

The SIC provides a working basis of classification of the content of the technical advancement of the organism so that the several segments of the wide spectrum of U.S. Industry which may be interested in the particular innovation may be identified. However, the *raison d' etre* of the patent is the specific innovation it represents; and in order for that specific innovation to be considered for incorporation in the production process by the patenting organism itself or other organisms, the contribution to technological feasibility contained in the innovation has to be specified. We discussed in Chapter 3 the technological feasibility of an idea in terms of technometric structure (see page 55). Innovation profile-construction efforts, in order to be meaningful, should reflect the technometric structure of the resources at the disposal of the organism. Thus the patent may involve an improvement of the current manufacturing process, say increasing the speed of the airplanes from subsonic to transsonic, thereby affecting the behavioral properties of the resources; or it may involve a radical departure from the current manufacturing process, say changing from planes to rockets, thereby incorporating the structural propensities of the resources. This type of distinction between the potential impacts of the patent application is essential for consideration of using the patent by the patenting organism itself or other customers of the patent.

(B) CUSTOMER: (1) DEPARTMENTAL INFORMATION

We now turn from the considerations of the content of the patent novelty to the customers of the same. We may also look upon the distinction involved in terms of manufacturing the patent novelty on the one hand, and marketing it on the other.

(1) The behavioral properties of the resources are traditionally in the custody of the research component of the organism. The technological advancement represented in the innovation by the researcher will have to be translated in terms of the impact of the innovation, generally by some other component of the organism. (2) Similarly, structural propensities of the resources are also in some measure available from the research component, although this too will have to be translated.

The translators of (1) and (2) may generally be the custodians of the patents of the organism. These custodians can help determine whether certain *specific results of technometric structure* should be made available for its own future use, or for the current use of other organisms. Distinction will have to be made between the efforts to patent the quantum jumps, or linear extensions, of the behavioral properties of the resources of the organism, on the one hand; and the specific efforts to find the match between the needs of other organisms and the patents at the disposal of the organism. The former are the concern of the patent lawyers; the latter that of the patent-licensing group.

(3) Technical support available to the organism to facilitate the translation of ideas into output may be identified from the records of the development component of the traditional research and development activity of the organism. Further, the series of small improvements that are in progress in the different parts of the production component of the organism also needs to be taken into account. It has been found in several instances that, the so-called production improvements have really been small-scale efforts to initiate or innovate technical support for the translation of ideas into output of the organism.

(4) *Sales record* is the backbone of the information for PTPD (Periodic Table of Product Diversification). The quantity and the value of sales of particular products at particular times and over particular periods of time, provide invaluable insight into the acceptance by the market of the different end-results of combinations of capabilities that the organism has to offer. As we said earlier, PTPD would provide guideline indications of necessary improvement of current products and/or introduction of new products, as are indicated by the respective stages of growth.

(5) *Marketing research* information provides the organism with both output information and organism information. "Who is producing what?" can be very useful in checking out the innovation profile that emerges from the particular records of the organism itself.

(6) *Purchasing* information can indicate the extent of interdependence of the organism with other organisms, both in the past and in the present. This would be valuable to decide upon the relative *in*dependence that the organism can claim in its pursuit of quantum jumps in the behavioral properties of resources. Some of the current supply of inputs may either have to extend their capabilities to meet the new situation, or be replaced; and the very fact of the supply of inputs by other organisms at the present time indicates either the plentitude of the required input supplies in their possession, or their nonentry into the same adjacent field of operations.

(7) The *financing arrangements* required to facilitate the exchange of the organism with the outside world can be reflected in the analysis of accounts receivable. It may very well be that the rate of delinquency, the cost of pursuit of delinquent accounts, etc., indicate the advisability of provision of credit and financing arrangements by the organism itself. The impact of financing arrangements on the innovation profile construction is in the direction of much-wanted realism. Thus, the built-in rate of obsolescence of automobiles has led to a flourishing market in credit-acceptance business sponsored by the manufacturers themselves.

How can these differing pieces of information be put together from the point of view of innovation profile construction efforts?

It is clear that there are two types of information available: (a) output (product) information; and (B) customer information. We saw on page 163 that the SIC (Standard Industrial Classification) is the cornerstone of intelligence retrieval based on the two types of major information relating to patents and customers. This logic can be extended from patents to products. Further, the customer information itself can be related to the product information: *a customer is a customer for outputs (products)*. The organism manufactures outputs, and/or exchanges (sells) the outputs —

whether or not it manufactures them. The organism may have a patent relating to the manufacture or modification of an output — present or potential. Thus, we can conceptually extend the logic of using SIC to meaningfully relate patent and customer information to product and customer information as well.

OBSTRUCTIONS TO INTERNAL FLOW OF INFORMATION

While the advantages of coordinating the information in the custody of each department of the organism are apparent, there are barriers, both visible and invisible, imposed on such interdepartmental information flow.

REASONS FOR DEPARTMENTALIST ISOLATION

Why are these barriers interposed between the profile construction efforts for the organism as a whole, and the individual activities of the components of the organism?

First, because of *perspective* differences. The perspective of the profile constructor is that of the organism as a whole, as well as the organism in the future vis-à-vis the past. The predominant preoccupations of the components of the organism, on the other hand, tend to run in separate circles with themselves as centers, instead of the organism. A by-product of specialization of functions, the departmentalization permits sectional efficiencies, but also runs the risk of the parts pursuing their atomistic viewpoints instead of the organismic viewpoint. Charged with the responsibility of justifying its own separate existence and activities, each component of the organism tends to adopt a particular form of collecting, recording, and analyzing information relating to its own activities.

Second, because of incompatible *performance criteria,* quite often the claim is made that the performance criteria of one component cannot either be easily established or easily administered: because there are "a lot of intangibles" entering into the conception and execution of such activity. The effect of the intangible, but nevertheless quite concrete, influence of continuous advertising on the current and future sales, the great amount of "worrying" that the sales executives from vice presidents down to salesman have to perform before sales are generated, the somewhat mysterious, "corporate disposition" toward new acquisitions — are some of the almost occult considerations claimed by the activities of the components to justify, maintain, and perpetuate collection, recording, and analysis of information pertaining to the activity of the components of the organism.

Third, because of *inertia* and *inhibition*. In addition to the different perspectives that separate the components of the organism from each other, and the differences in the systems of information maintenance used by the different components in the interest of their survival, the factor of inertia, of sheer inertia, for intercomponent communications, as well as the accompanying inhibition from fear of the unknown in venturing across well-recognized responsibility lines, contribute significantly to the innumerable, invisible, but effective, doors erected between the information and the profile construction.

AN EMPIRICAL SITUATION

Inquiry into the possible ways of improving the performance of a product group, authorized by a vice-president, revealed that there were at least five major components of the organism, each competitively bidding to supplant each other, in an effort to answer the basic question: How best can the customer be served? (1) There was the inspection of production performed at the plant level, properly reviewed by the plant management; (2) there was the overall organismic policing of quality performance capabilities and records, including those at the plant level; (3) there was a whole group of performance engineers, whose job it was to maintain close liaison with the customer, including the conduct of "experiments" on the actual performance of outputs in the customer facilities; (4) there was the research group charged with the responsibility of identifying, measuring, and improving parameters of performance of the output; (5) and there was the marketing component of the organism, which had to follow through with the comparison of promise vis-à-vis performance of the major outputs, to the satisfaction of the customer.

The plant location was about 400 miles via relatively inaccessible air route from the organismic policing of output performance activity, which in turn, was about 300 miles away from the research facility; the "experiments" on the customer facility were being conducted about 2,500 to 2,800 miles away from all the other three; and, the headquarters of marketing activity was 300 to 500 miles away from the plant, the policing, and the research activities, and 3,000 miles away from the "experimental activity." Close scrutiny of the elaborate records maintained by the different groups revealed, for instance, that the "experimental" data lacked conspicuously certain measurements needed to make adequate comparisons of the promises vis-à-vis the performance. The research efforts were relatively esoteric in that their accent was more on the fundamental performance of basic materials and outputs, than the more specific questions of performance of individual products. The plant was generating reams of information, with almost no reference to criteria by which many of the figures would be judged or it would be possible to judge. The organismic policing effort tried to reach out for standards that may be meaningful from the point of view of most of the plants and most of the activities: within the context of this search, its immediate relevance to the question of customer satisfaction was far from direct or established. The physical distances, no doubt, contributed heavily to the lack of communications between the components themselves. There was almost an inhibitory effort upon communication because of the overlapping of the objectives of the different components, and the fear that logical disclosure the these disparate functions may lead to heavy curtailment, if not total abolishment, of those activities which were at least in part redundant.

CIRS, A CENTRAL SYSTEM

How can these barriers be effectively removed so that they are no longer means of separation, but means of communication between and among the components of the organism?

(1) The *organismic*, instead of atomistic, perspective of the information gathered, (2) The *interdependence* of the different pieces of information from the point of view of "intelligence" of the organism as a whole, (3) The *independence* of each contribution to the central source, the strength and weakness of the system as a whole depending upon the strength and weakness of the component pieces of information, and (4) The *accessibility* of the central reservoir of information to *all* the contributing components of the organism, insofar as the individual activities of the components can be aided, facilitated, and improved by the overview provided by a centralized system of constructing intelligence out of information.

COORDINATION OF INTERNAL INFORMATION

We sketch in Figure 22 the profile of CIRS (Central Intelligence Retrieval System). The information within the purview of the different components of the organism is broadly classified into two sections: (I) Technometric structure, and (II) PTPD. While the PTPD is by-and-large concerned with present output, and technometric structure with potential outputs, there is understandably a crossover between the lines. For instance, Production supplies information relating to technical support for both present outputs (PTPD group) and for potential outputs (technometric structure group). Figure 22 highlights contributions of the different

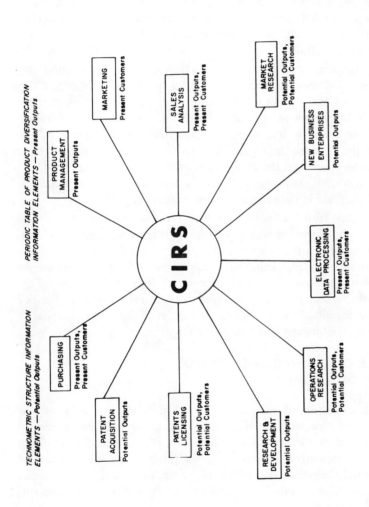

Figure 22. CENTRAL INTELLIGENCE RETRIEVAL SYSTEM.

components of the organism, along with the functional description of the activities. Thus, research is associated with both behavioral properties and structural propensities, while purchasing is associated with other organisms' supply capabilities. Development is associated with technical support, while sales analysis, with present output portfolio, and so on. Electronic data processing is associated with analysis of present outputs and customers, while operations research, with conceptual contributions to innovation profile construction efforts — basically to the potential outputs.

The components of the organism which generate information can, with little additional effort, provide the input for intelligence in CIRS. CIRS can guarantee that every input can be retrieved at par, so that whether the input is from Development, or from Purchasing or Financial Arrangements, it will be available intact on call. Quite possibly, the return will be more than at par because the Central System that CIRS is brings together so much information about the many parts of the organism that the CIRS participants will find answers and evaluations which could never be satisfactorily obtained in the several activity areas separately.

It is this truly cooperative effort on the part of the several components of the organism which will, through the coordinated codification of information synthesis enable the generation of intelligence — insights into interrelationships otherwise unavailable — for the organism; on which intelligence, reasonable innovation can be constructed in terms of the capabilities of the organism, and the resources available to it on the one hand, and the acceptability *of* outputs, and accessibility *to* the outputs of the organism by the outside world, on the other.

INTELLIGENCE OF INNOVATION EFFORTS OF COMPETITIVE ORGANISMS

Implementation of innovation profile depends not only on the technometric structure, and technical support relating to the resources of the organism, and its own tempo of innovation, but also on the tempo of innovation of competitive organisms. CIRS provides an ideal means of effectively putting together the pieces of information that are available, which reveal a large amount of useful information about the tempo of competitive organisms.

A good starting point is the current output portfolios of different organisms, particularly the competitive organisms. The types of products, the names of products, the locations of the manufacturing facilities of the outputs — all are generally available from the open literature. The United States Government Census of Manufactures provides a large amount of this type of information, without identifying the individual organisms engaged in the manufacture of outputs. Thus, it is possible to know the regional distribution of the origin of shipments of major manufactured outputs. The organism has available from its own records, its share in such a regional distribution. Knowing the whole, and one part, it is conceptually feasible to develop a better appreciation about the other parts which contribute to the whole.

An important source of information about impending activities of other organisms in terms of entry into new fields of manufacture, and/or improvement of existing fields, is the organism's own sales forces. Granted that such information has to be taken with a grain of salt — a large grain of salt — nevertheless, the very fact that new beginnings are envisaged in associated lines of activity by competitive organisms is an important starting point. Information from the traditional marketing intelligence sources is also another important element in assessing the tempo of innovation of competitive organisms. Exchanges of information at a more technical level are obtained in the professional society meetings, based on which certain early indications of competitive innovation plans of organisms can be detected. Trade magazines, and handbooks of different segments of the industry, systematic compilation of organismic information by service organizations — are all important sources which provide information about the tempo of competitive organisms in matters of innovation.

SIC-BASED CODING OF CIRS ENTRIES

How can these different types of information be standardized in some fashion which will (1) take advantage of most sources of information and (2) which will be generally applicable to most economic activities in the United States?

Starting with the seven-digit product code of SIC, we can indicate by a suffix whenever reference is made to any product which merits a "line" in the Census of Manufactures. For instance, SIC Product 2013111 — sweet pickled of dry cured pork — is given a *suffix* of 0 to read 20131110 to stand for all references to the particular product, namely sweet pickled or dry cured pork. The sales by the particular organism of sweet pickled or dry cured pork would be coded 20131110 for CIRS entries.

Similarly, when we refer, not to the product but the manufacturer, we may use another suffix, 1: 20131111 stands for *manufacturer* of sweet pickled or dry cured pork. While the 0 indicates the finished product, there will be need to refer to the *raw material* for manufacturing the finished product. Cucumbers for making pickles is an example. While it is feasible to refer to cucumbers by an eight-digit code with a 0 in the last place, its relation to the sweet-pickled or dry-cured-pork industry would not be obvious in such a frame of reference. Therefore, in referring to cucumbers as raw material for the sweet-pickled or dry-cured-pork industry, we may code it as 20131112, the 2 in the last place referring to a *raw material* for the industry.

Competitive organisms may be interested in entering the sweet-pickled or dry-cured-pork industry. Announcements in the trade magazines, in regular advertisements, tidbits picked up at professional meetings, etc., may be coded appropriately to form informative bits in CIRS. These informations relate to what may be termed *activity plans* of organisms, and may be given another code, say 3. Thus, 20131113 would indicate activity plans of the organism(s) to enter the sweet-pickled or dry-cured-pork industry. Incidentally, the organism's own interest in entering a new field may be identified by similar coding device.

What if the organism is a seller of sweet pickled or dry cured pork, without being a manufacturer? We may assign suffix 4 to indicate a *seller only* of the product. Now, if the organism is both a manufacturer and seller, two passes on electronic data-processing equipment will be necessary — first to identify the manufacturer, and second to identify the seller. From the results of the two separate passes on the electronic data-processing equipment, we shall presumably have a large pile from which organisms who are both manufacturers and sellers have to be manually identified. Since this category is extremely important — an organism who is both a manufacturer and a seller is definitely preferable to an organism which is either one or the other — we may prefer to give a separate suffix, say 5, to indicate a manufacturer-and-seller. Thus, 20131115 would represent an organism which is both a *manufacturer and seller* of sweet pickled or dry cured pork.

Considerable attention was given in PTPD to customers, and major customers. They have to be identified in a standard fashion, which can be done by adding the suffix 6 to the SIC code. Thus 20131116 would mean *end-users* of sweet pickled or dry cured pork, e.g., Chinese restaurants.

Reference was made earlier to a hypothetical patent relating to a curing process which may be useful to the sweet-pickled or dry-cured-pork industry. It may be necessary in some instances to have special facilities which would permit the use of the patent. The fact that an organism has, among its resources, farm facilities may possibly induce it to go into the sweet-pickled or dry-cured-pork business, although at the current time, no pigs are included in the farm livestock. In this instance, the existence of a *facility* for entering into (a part of) the industry would be of significance to the organism if it has a patent to offer to improve or innovate the process of curing, or if the organism were interested in identifying potential competition, and assessing its importance. We shall designate the existence of a facility which near-uniquely qualifies the organism to enter an industry by the suffix 7. Thus, 20131117 would mean that the organism possesses some near-unique facility for entering the sweet-pickled or dry-cured-pork industry.

We set forth in Figure 23 the SIC-based coding for CIRS entries.

Sausages and other prepared meat products

Sweet pickled or dry cured pork

INDUSTRY NUMBER	PRODUCT NUMBER	SUFFIX	
2013	111		
2013	111	0	Pickled or cured Pork, the Product
2013	111	1	Pickled or cured Pork, the Manufacturer of
2013	111	2	Pickled or cured Pork, the Raw Material for
2013	111	3	Pickled or cured Pork, the Activity Plans of Potential Entrant Into
2013	111	4	Pickled or cured Pork, the Seller of
2013	111	5	Pickled or cured Pork, the Manufacturer-and-Seller of
2013	111	6	Pickled or cured Pork, End-User of·
2013	111	7	Pickled or cured Pork, the Possessor of Near-Unique Facility for

Figure 23. SIC-BASED CODING FOR CIRS ENTRIES.

There has to be additional coding provision for the *reliability of information* that is fed into CIRS. Thus, for instance, a wild rumor ought to be distinguished from a government statistics report. Again, the issuance of codified figures for an industry, or a segment of industry, by a responsible research organization should be accorded a standing perhaps as high as the government statistics themselves, but certainly higher than that for wild rumors. Provision can be made for such classification of reliability of information by means of a *reliability index,* ranging from 01 through 99.

ILLUSTRATIVE RANKING OF TEMPO OF INNOVATION OF COMPETITIVE ORGANISMS

How can we meaningfully assess the various and sundry information we have obtained about the tempo of innovation of competitive organisms?

An illustrative ranking procedure is indicated in Figure 24. Two units of score on a scale of 100 equal 1 Rank Unit. The first rank corresponds to a score of 99. If an organism is (1) a manufacturer-and-seller, (2) an end-user of the output, and (3) has acquired raw-material facilities, that would yield the highest score possible: 99. By virtue of an entry of the answer "yes" corresponding to the suffix 5, the entries corresponding to suffixes 1 and 4 are automatically made redundant. Similarly, by the fact that the organism is a manufacturer, whatever near-unique facilities are required for the particular manufacture are considered operationally available to the organism. Against this background of the highest strength, what potential competition does the organism face?

The chances are, that if someone is *selling* sweet and dried pork today and has an eye on entering into the *manufacturing end* of the business, he would be a potentially strong possibility as a competitor. Add to it the availability of raw materials and near-unique facilities for such manufacture, plus the fact that he is an end-user — a Chinese restaurant owner who also has a large farm suitable to raise pigs, and who is currently selling sweet and dried pork — the second-best possible combination of circumstances are available to this organism. It is accorded the second highest rank, corresponding to a score of 97.

From now on, *a priori* considerations heavily affect the applicability of ranking procedures. For instance, in Figure 24, we give a score of 95 and a rank of 03 to the organism which has all the same elements as the second-highest ranking organism except the near-unique facility. Score 93

Rank	Manufacturer Only Suffix 1	Seller Only Suffix 4	Manufacturer-and-Seller Suffix 5	End-User Suffix 6	Raw Material Suffix 2	Facility Suffix 7	Activity Plans Suffix 3	Score
01	0	0	1	1	1	0	0	99
02	0	1	0	1	1	1	1	97
03	0	1	0	1	1	0	1	95
04	0	1	0	1	0	1	1	93
05	0	1	0	0	1	1	1	91
06	0	0	0	1	1	1	1	89
07	0	1	0	0	0	1	1	87
08	0	1	0	1	0	0	1	85
09	0	0	0	1	0	1	1	83
10	0	0	0	1	1	0	1	81
11	0	0	0	0	1	1	1	79

Figure 24. ILLUSTRATIVE RANKING OF TEMPO OF INNOVATION.

and rank 04 is given to the organism which does not have the raw materials, but has the near-unique facilities. In other words, there is an implicit ranking of preferences from among the factors necessary for the implementation of the innovation. Near-unique facility is given a lower rank than raw material, and raw material is given a lower rank than the fact of the organism being an end-user.

That is why the score increases from 91 to 93 when the element of end-use is introduced; from 93 to 95 when the availability of raw material is introduced; and from 95 to 97 when the near-unique facility is introduced. In all of these considerations, the organism was already a seller of the output in question. When that element is taken out, the score declines from 97 to 89. In other words, the fact of the organism being a seller is given a weight of 8 on a scale of 100. When the elements of end-use and availability of raw material are exchanged for the fact of being a seller only, the score goes down from 89 to 87. Reintroducing the element of end-use but simultaneously removing the availability of raw material reduces the score by 2 from 87 to 85. The removal of the element of end-use, leaving raw-material availability, near-unique facility, and active plans, decreases the score from 89 to 79.

Admittedly, these rankings are only for illustrative purposes. But they do highlight the effect of innovation of elements *in combination,* over and above their respective individual contributions.

By judicious data processing of CIRS information, *all* organisms in the sweet-pickled and dry-cured-pork industry, for instance, can be scored and ranked. It may reveal that the organism currently employed in the industry ought not to be in it; and that there are several other organisms which are capable of giving strong competition, by virtue of great advantages of resources combinations. By the same token, CIRS intelligence may indicate that the organism should enter into several other fields in which it has substantial potential assets. In short, the CIRS approach to the problem provides an objective measure for translating various and sundry pieces of information obtained from varied sources into an intelligent ordering of the capabilities of resources available to the organism itself, or its potential competition.

PART IV

PHILOSOPHY OF ALLOCATION

You had that action and counteraction which,
in the natural and in the political world,
from the reciprocal struggle of discordant
powers draws out the harmony of the universe.

EDMUND BURKE (1729-1797)
Reflections on the Revolution in France (1790)

We are two halves of a pair of scissors, when
apart, Pecksniff, but together we are something.

CHARLES DICKENS (1812-1870)
Martin Chuzzlewit

There is light in shadow and shadow in light,
And black in the blue of the sky.

LUCY LARCOM (1826-1893)
"Black in Blue Sky"

CHAPTER SEVEN

CONCOMITANT COALITIONS IN BUSINESS BARGAINING: WITH AND AGAINST THE SAME PLAYER(S)

Well-begun is half-done. The beginning by being good militates against its own continuance. It is as though the process of beginning has in it the seeds of its own opposition and eventual replacement.

This opposition is in fact ever-present. Whether we consider love or light, inherent in love is hate, and inherent in light is shadow. Yet these traces of the opposites are discernible only under perceptive analysis or in the case of breakdowns, when the tension of the opposites becomes too devastating to be controlled by the organism.

These opposites are a fact of life. There are no "absolute" attitudes. Thus, statements of the form: A "absolutely" loves B, or B "absolutely" hates C, are at best inaccurate; at worst, a horrible camouflage for half-understood notions. At the height of A's love for B, there is *simultaneously*

185

present A's hate for B; only it is not perceptible, just like the stars at midday.

Part of the reason why the opposites are not always perceived is the sheer complexity of the levels of *being* and *doing* of the organism. If the organism is a person, the levels of being can roughly be classified into the conscious, the subconscious, the unconscious. Of the three, the conscious can be compared to the relatively small fraction of a submerged iceberg that is visible. Underneath, the subconscious discloses its profile in part through the media of dreams, covert acts of hostility, and so on; while it may take the violent crashing of the ship of life itself to reveal fathoms of the unconscious. Even this categorization into three merely highlight how little we know of ourselves, of what makes us "tick"; but we do know enough not to characterize the practices, perspectives, and perceptions of the overt and the visible as those of the self as a whole.

If our knowledge of the levels of being is meager, that of the levels of doing is still less. Yearning is a feature of man's aspirations and even at the level of basic activity characteristics, there are built-in instability, and inherent opposition. Built-in instability arises out of the yearning level, actuating the organism for more — whether it be of earning or of enjoying. And there is inherent opposition. The necessity of earning is generally opposed to the process of enjoying; and current enjoying is opposed to future enjoying, because in the satisfaction of the current needs are the dissatisfaction with the current, and the seeds of the future wants.

These concepts of earning and enjoying are quite general. For a personal organism, the objective of earning can be tangible — money, property, or intangible — friendship, prestige. For an industrial organism, the objectives of earning can be tangible — sales, profits, or intangible — goodwill, prestige. And for a military organism, the objectives of earning can be tangible — retaliatory weapon systems, or intangible — avoidance of direct warfare.

Let us consider Edmund Burke's "action and counteraction which .... from the reciprocal struggle of discordant powers draws out the harmony of the universe." "The reciprocal struggle of discordant powers" of arms for use and arms for nonuse, "draws out the harmony of the universe," which harmony is generated by the avowed opposition of the separate organisms, successfully struggling to survive. This reciprocal struggle is not confined to the military or to the present. The Cross and Crescent were locked in mortal combat in the eleventh, twelfth, and thirteenth centuries: the discordant powers were not as much military organisms as religious organisms. But harmony of sorts was drawn out of what appeared to be a fight to the finish; and the Cross and the Crescent do continue as separate organisms, successfully struggling to survive.

Whether or not militant forms are assumed by the discordant powers, as in the Crusades and the Cold War, the inherent discordance underlying the organisms' individual existence is undeniable. It is this discord that led to the détente ensuring the survival of the organisms of Islam and Christianity. Does the existence of the détente suddenly spring a new fact of life? Or, does it merely bring to light what was always there, viz., the basic opposition in the fighting organism itself, which simultaneously seeks to annihilate and accommodate?

Perhaps this opposition may be viewed constructively. In the words of Dickens quoted at the beginning of this chapter, "We are two halves of a pair of scissors, when apart, Pecksniff, but together we are something." While the organism's alter ego seeking to annihilate, and the organism's anti-ego seeking to accommodate, would when apart be ruinous, but together would be creatively constructive. Here we view the opposing interests, or Burke's discordant powers, as imbued with personality; yet they inhabit the same organism; therefore that occupancy should be emphasized. So we shall call them alter ego and anti-ego, to signify that they represent opposing interests while simultaneously inhabiting the same organism.

Industrial and military organisms have to live with inherent oppositions, just as individual human beings. However, they command more resources and possibly more resourcefulness than the individual, to live with directions which are inherently opposed to each other. For the same reason, untenability of opposing activities of segments of the same organism may go undetected for much longer than in the case of an individual in whom the untenability would be detected much earlier under similar pressures.

The Periodic Table of Diversification (PTPD) suggests to the management what outputs are required to be introduced and when, in order to maintain and improve the organism's product portfolio. The Central Intelligence Retrieval System (CIRS) facilitates a systematic look at the plans and programs of other organisms as they may impinge upon the organism's own present and future efforts. The present and future efforts of the organism, as well as the efforts of the organism vis-á-vis other organisms emerging from PTPD (Chapter 5) and CIRS (Chapter 6) viewpoints may appear to be unequivocally opposed. How can the organism incorporate this inherent opposition into policies which use today's information for tomorrow's products?

EMPIRICAL REFERENTS OF INHERENT OPPOSITION

If inherent opposition is basic to the very being and doing of organisms, how can they live with, instead of die from, such polarity?

Three types of instances of inherent opposition of interests and manipulations in industrial organisms may be cited. (A) The opposition may go undetected in relatively large organisms — industrial, military, commercial, or institutional. (B) The opposition may be manipulated and even fostered intentionally in organisms both large and small, to the advantage of the organism. (C) The opposing interests may involve more than one organism; as a member of present and/or potential partners in coalitions, the organism can deliberately act in concert with other organisms simultaneously for and against the same member, including itself.

These empirical referents, designated respectively as A1, A2, A3, B1, C1, are only illustrative of the phenomenon of inherent opposition of interests. In the first four instances, the opposition of interests was *internal* to the organism; in the third, the opposition involved *external* organisms as well.

MARKETING VERSUS MANUFACTURING (A1)

It was found in a high-production, high-inventory, poor-shipment situation that the production engineers pursued relentlessly their objective of increasing production as much as possible; while the sales engineers kept on selling everything the organism was actually manufacturing, planning to manufacture, could conceivably manufacture, and could hardly conceive manufacturing. Both groups were quite surprised to learn that they were not exactly pulling in the same direction. Operations research approach to the problem demonstrated clearly that as much as 18 percent of the total production, the pride and joy of the production engineers, contributed only as little as 2.5 – 3.0 percent of the total sales revenue; while a sizable portion of the sales orders brought in by the sales engineers was for outputs not even remotely in the "think" stage. Owing in part to the technical problem of production, including the state-of-the-art of that particular manufacturing process, and in part to the sales commitments made by the sales engineers on nothing more substantial than a hopeful disposition, any correspondence between the sales orders written and the units for sale was not necessarily intentional. With little correspondence between the supply of products and the demand for them, it was small wonder that there arose simultaneously, large production, high inventory, and delayed shipment.

SIX TO ACQUIRE AND ONE-HALF TO SELL (A2)

Similar functional fragmentation was observed with respect to patents in a large organism. There were six different departments engaged in the creation, fostering, and validation of claims on patentable ideas. (1) There was the research and development department, with a large staff of researchers engaged continuously in the process of creation of patentable ideas. (2) There was the research and development patent liaison function, trying to keep up with the emerging ideas, and the areas in which such ideas were directly available.

(3) There was the team of patent lawyers constantly preparing for presentation and presenting to the United States Patent Office claims for issuance of patents. (4) There was the department stationed in Washington, for the investigation of new patentable areas of research as well as for keeping abreast of the latest changes in the process for obtaining patents. (5) Another department located on the same site as the research and development facility kept track of the actual patents issued, both to the organism and to competing organisms. (6) Further, there was the counterpart of the research and development, or its "lobby," 400 miles away, functioning as a separate department. Through this liaison, the research personnel presumably had direct access to the management of the organism.

With at least these six separate departments all engaged in the process of creating and generating new patentable ideas and patents for the organism, only *one* department of the company was concerned with disposing of patents which were not usable by the organism, and even that (single, lone) department spent less than *half* its time on this function. However, there were occasionally other departments that got into the act in trying to lend a hand.

CONFLICTING ORGANISMIC MANEUVERS: BUY XYZ COMPANY, SELL TO XYZ COMPANY (A3)

Industrial organisms, if sufficiently large, may find that component parts sometimes pursue conflicting policies in unknowing opposition to organismic policies; occasionally they even ignore them. The components work for the organism when they survive as component parts of the organism, thus enabling the survival of the organism itself. But their efficient efforts to survive as parts may set their sectional survival policies in opposition to those of the organism, resulting in the components working *against* the organism: *for* in survival, but *against* in policy; or, *for* in being but *against* in doing.

Thus, it was that the patent lawyers who were interested in the job of preparing for presentation, and presentation to the U.S. Patent Office, patentable ideas generated by the organism, suggested to XYZ Company that a particular patent in the possession of the organism was potentially extremely valuable to the said company. This led to some interest on the part of the XYZ Company, which wanted to explore the matter further. At this point, the department formally charged with the patents had to be informed. And this was done in an informal manner at a chance meeting in the elevator after lunch.

Unknown to both these departments, there was a third department of the organism which was working closely with the XYZ Company. Object: acquisition of XYZ Company by the organism. It so happened that at the chance meeting, this particular department was also represented. But for this chance meeting, and the chance mentioning of the "XYZ Company," it is unlikely that the simultaneous maneuvers by the different parts of the organism in direct conflict with each other would have come to light even at that time. Here, there was the effort to sell to XYZ Company on the one hand, and to buy XYZ Company altogether on the other.

CONFLICTING FUNCTIONAL ALIGNMENT: PARTNERS IN PRODUCTION: OPPONENTS IN SALES (B1)

The conflicting organismic maneuvers with respect to XYZ Company were in part, the result of lack of communication, and consequent pursuit of sectional objectives without regard to the organismic objectives.

The assignment of production of constituent parts, or constitutent groups of products, to other firms is a well-known practice. However, competition by X_1 with Y for sales of products supplied it by Y, while both are components of X, is not common.

A conscious effort on the part of an organism to *intentionally* foster conflicting functional alignment to further the objective of the organism itself is possible, particularly when the component units of the organism are physically separated and production and sales are channeled differently. In an instance of corporate merger, such a conflicting functional alignment was observed.

Organism X absorbed Organism Y. The outputs offered by organisms X and Y overlapped in some measure. It was found that Y had certain advantages over X in production of part of the overlapping segment carried on at X_1, one of the production facilities of X. Now that Y had become a component of X, X_1, which had been part of X, became kindred to Y. However, the organism X decided to manufacture some of the output originally produced by X_1, using the facilities of Y. Thus, in the instance of production, X_1 and Y were *partners*.

However, when it came to sales of these products, owing to the brand loyalty which Y commanded, there was direct *competition* with X_1 for the sales of its products. Since both X_1 and Y became component parts of X, the organismic objective was to improve the sales of outputs of X, whether manufactured at X_1, or Y. If offered as a completed line of X, that line would comprise both the outputs of X_1 and Y. However, in order to take advantage of the established brand loyalties for outputs of Y, it was decided that the X_1 outputs would continue to be offered as X_1 outputs and Y outputs as Y outputs in their respective sales areas, X_1 competitive with Y although X_1 and Y were both now parts of X.

The organism adopted the policy of conflicting functional alignment because: although (i) the partnership in production between X_1 and Y would lead to decreased costs in production to the organism X; (ii) however, the opposition between the outputs of X_1 and Y in bidding for the same market would increase total sales of X because of the brand loyalties which had been traditionally established.

The conflicting functional alignment took the form of partnership in production between X_1 and Y, and simultaneous opposition in sales between X_1 and Y. The payoff to the organism X itself would comprise: (i) The increase in *individual* sales of brand X_1 and brand Y over the sales of brand X incorporating X_1 and Y, (ii) The savings in production costs by manufacturing X_1 items in Y, and (iii) The excess of (i) over (ii) if X_1 were to make a side payment to Y for the savings in production costs, leading to the increase in sales revenue, made possible by their coalition.

CONFLICTING COALITION EFFORTS: MANUFACTURER-DISTRIBUTORS: OTHER MANUFACTURERS-DISTRIBUTORS (C1)

In both the instance of conflicting organismic maneuvers and conflicting functional alignment, it was one and the same organism which was playing against itself. In the coalition efforts to be considered now, the organism could *deliberately* act in concert with *other* organisms simultaneously for and against the same member, including itself.

The organism decided to manufacture in $(n-1)$ plants, instead of n plants. The distribution of the output of the organism was via *distributors*. Owing to the special nature of the output, special handling was required, such as special types of vehicles and satisfaction of interstate regulations. The permission given the distributor by the States to transport the output from one place to another hinged on the support of the organism who manufactured the output. In other words, the manufacturer was essential for the distributor to obtain the license to operate, and the distributor was essential for the manufacturer for transporting the output.

In the light of the decision by the organism to discontinue production of the output in one of its n plants, there was a question of supplying the customers who were previously supplied by the newly eliminated plant. If the distributors were to obtain their supplies from the remaining $(n-1)$ plants, it would entail additional effort on their part. Even if the distributors were willing to expend the additional effort, in several instances, plants in other states were involved — to transport from which, licenses had to be obtained to comply with interstate regulations. The organism was willing to do its part in facilitating the issuance of such interstate operating permits. But the problem of additional compensation for the distributors for their inconvenience, in having to obtain supplies from $(n-1)$ plants instead of n plants, had to be settled.

The distributors wore more than just the one hat of transportation. (1) The distributors were customers of the organism, because they themselves consumed part of the output they purchased. (2) They were *transportation agents* for the organism, in which capacity they would be recognized as, say, XYZ Transportation Company. (3) Owing to the far-flung nature of demand for the particular output of the organism, and owing to the frequent demand for supply of small quantities at short notice, the organism found it advantageous to build several warehouses in different parts of the country. The distributors also acted as *warehouse agents,* in which capacity they would be recognized as XYZ warehouse keepers of the organism. (4) The distributors performed their role as distributors, buying from the organism at a particular price, and selling, on their own, to customers for profit; in which capacity they were XYZ distributors. (5) In addition, the organism appointed the distributors as *ad hoc* agents of the organism. Thus, if a special demand arose for a particular type of output of the organism, and the demand were placed on the organism, instead of the distributors, the organism would instruct the closest distributors to act as the special agents of the organism, and perform the delivery of the outputs to the customers.

These five different hats worn simultaneously by the distributors made the negotiations of additional compensation somewhat complicated. The second of these roles was crucial, both because time was of the essence in shipments, and because freight costs often made the difference in pennies between profit and loss. The fifth role was assumed when the organism authorized emergency sales by the distributors on its behalf to the organism's customers far away from the plant, but near the warehouse used by the distributors. These sales to the customers of the organism will be designated *Resale I,* distinguished from sales to distributor customers, *Resale II.* Distributor revenue comprises resale revenues I and II and backhaul revenue obtained by acting as carriers for other customers enroute from the warehouse to the plant.[1]

Operations research approach to this problem led to departure from traditional solutions. It was known that the marketing department's recommendation to placate the distributors by compensating them for their "added inconvenience" in having to draw supplies from $(n-1)$ plants instead of n, did not take into account the several possibilities of manipulating inherent oppositions in the situation: e.g., opposition between manufacturer and distributors, between other manufacturers and distributors, etc. A systematic investigation of the problem led to a conceptual innovation to which we turn next.

CONCOMITANT COALITION — A NEW CONCEPT

The traditional treatment of the situation of inherent opposition discussed on pages 191-3 would recognize three types of coalitions. I: *Status quo or distribution coalition*: In this arrangement, the organism enters into coalition with* the distributors against the customers. In fact, the contemplated additional compensation to the distributors is precisely the subject of this coalition consideration. The cost to the customer when the output is obtained through distributors is generally higher than if it is directly obtained from the manufacturer. However, faced with the possibility of still additional cost to the customers, resulting from the additional payment to the distributors for supply from $(n-1)$ plants instead of n plants, the organism may decide to ship directly to the customers. This leads to coalition II: *No production or distribution coalition*. When the organism ships directly to customers, it is the coalition of the organism with customers against distributors.

So far, the problem has been viewed simply as a transportation

---

1 George K. Chacko, "Bargaining Strategy in a Production and Distribution Problem," *Operations Research* (November – December 1961), pp. 811-827.

* We refer to coalitions *with* and *against* where more than one organism is involved, as in the case of organism vis-à-vis distributors; as distinguished from coalitions *for* and *against* where one and the same organism is involved.

problem. Given the output in $(n-1)$ locations, instead of n locations, what arrangements can be made to transfer the shipment from the manufacturing sources to the customers?

A PRODUCTION-AND-DISTRIBUTION PROBLEM, NOT MERELY A TRANSPORTATION PROBLEM

However, it was found that the problem could be viewed as a production-and-distribution problem, instead of merely a transportation problem. Other manufacturers had production facilities located in and around the area which was served by the particular plant in which the production was to be discontinued. The organism could negotiate with other organisms to supply the distributor customers, thus saving warehousing costs. This would be a third type of coalition — *III: Production coalitions*: The company enters into coalition with other manufacturers against the distributors, or, more specifically, against the transportation aspect of the distributor services.

So far the customers were not considered as entering into the coalition picture. One of the contributions of the operations research approach to the problem was to focus attention on the customers instead of the distributors, for the bargaining strength of the distributors depended on the existence of the customers. If there were no customers, no matter how great an advantage the distributor might be able to command in transporting the output, warehousing the output, and reselling the output — on his own, or in behalf of the organism — it would be of no avail. This insight, provided by operations research, served to give an entirely different perspective to the problem. Hitherto, the traditional marketing approach had been to treat the distributors as "sacred cows" who must not be displeased, but had to be humored at any cost: because, without them, reasoned the traditional marketing approaches, there would be no sales. What the operations research approach pointed out was that with or without the distributors, if there were no customers, then there would be no sales at all.

Thus, the most important player whose favor was to be won turned out to be the customers. Since, without them there would be little justification for the output of the organism, the customers could be conceived as bargaining with the organism for additional compensation to induce them to buy directly from the organism, instead of the distributors, with the threat of buying the output from other sources. Knowing their indispensability to the distributors, the customers could be conceived as bargaining with the distributors for additional compensation for buying from them, instead of directly from the organism, or from the other manufacturing sources.

The operations research approach directed attention to the end points, the customers, instead of the intermediate points, the distributors: how many customers had to be wooed away from the distributors? Careful calculations (pages 199-203) showed that it was not essential to sell to all the distributor customers; it would be adequate if some of the customers could be persuaded to buy directly from the organism, instead of indirectly through the distributors, the exact requisite customer composition being a function of the objective of net profit of the organism.

How about the other manufacturers? Knowing the considerable freight savings realizable by the organism if shipments were made from the production facilities of other manufacturers, instead of the organism's own plants, the other manufacturers could be conceived as bargaining with the organism for additional compensation for agreeing to sell to the organism, with the threat of either sales to the competitors of the organism and/or to the customers directly.

At the same time, the organism may be conceived as entering into coalitions with both the customers and the production facility against the distributors who have heretofore been supplying the customers. These coalitions are different from the three sets of coalitions which were discussed previously. I: Status quo or distribution coalition; II: No production or distribution coalition; and III: Production coalition — all were coalitions in which "either-or" relationship holds. Thus, the company enters into a coalition with the distributors against customers; or with customers against distributors; or with other manufacturers against transportation facilities. In each of the three instances, the organism is either with or against. The choices are clear-cut; the alternatives are clear-cut; so are the decisions. These coalitions may be called *discrete coalitions,* to signify the fact that the alternatives are discrete; so are the choices.

CONCOMITANT COALITIONS AND DISCRETE COALITIONS

On the other hand, the organism's simultaneous entry into different coalitions with and against the same players is not an instance of discrete coalition. Coalitions of this kind may be referred to as *concomitant coalitions,* distinguished by the following features:

1. simultaneous entry into coalitions by players,
2. who band together for and against the same party at the same time, and
3. makes moves subject to the several objectives of the different coalitions, but

4. governed ultimately by the overriding principle of self-interest,

5. in order to achieve joint-profit-maximization

6. in a nonzero-sum game.[2]

In Figure 25 we represent the discrete and nondiscrete coalitions in the conflicting coalition efforts involving the manufacturer, distributors, and other manufacturers. Looking at the alternatives from the point of view of the organism, we notice that in one discrete coalition the organism enters into a coalition with the customers against the distributors. In the corresponding concomitant coalition situation however, we find that the organism enters into a coalition with the customers against other manufacturers on the one hand; and with other manufacturers against the customers on the other, both simultaneously.

In the discrete coalition the organism offers to sell directly to the customers at prices competitive with the ones that they were obtaining when they bought through the distributors. The advantage in price offered by the organism comes from what used to be the payment to the distributor for his services. In the nondiscrete coalition, or concomitant coalition situation, however, the organism enters into coalition with and against the customers; and with and against other manufacturers simultaneously.

The coalition arrangement of the organism with customers offers the payoff: the offer to sell direct to the customers. But in view of the simultaneity, this offer to sell direct to the customers is, ipso facto, a coalition against other manufacturers. At the same time, it is also a coalition against the distributors. On the other hand, the organism may enter into coalition arrangements with other manufacturers, offering to sell via other manufacturers, instead of direct to the customers. Since the least expensive sales to the customers are those made direct to them, with no intermediary, the organism-other manufacturers coalition is against the customers; it is also against the distributors.

Thus, we have two simultaneous four-member coalitions: The (i) organism with (ii) customers against (iii) other manufacturers, against (iv) distributors; and the (i) organism with (ii) other manufacturers, against (iii) customers, against (iv) distributors. In the discrete coalition situation, we have only one coalition.

We see in Figure 25 that all the concomitant coalitions considered are against the distributors. We can certainly consider situations in which the organism enters into coalitions with the distributors, the customers enter into coalitions with the distributors; other manufacturers enter into

---

[2] George K. Chacko, *op. ct.,* p. 817.

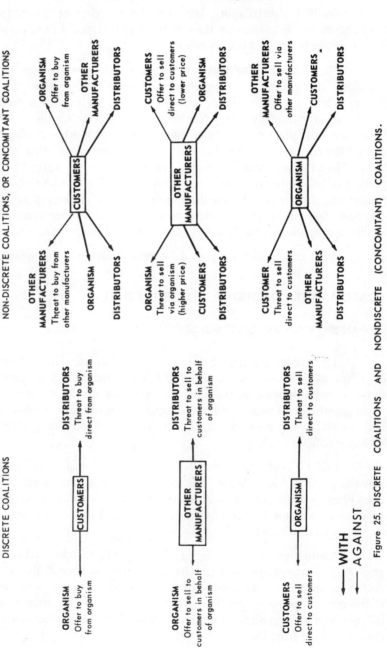

Figure 25. DISCRETE COALITIONS AND NONDISCRETE (CONCOMITANT) COALITIONS.

coalitions with the distributors. However, for purposes of illustration, we have chosen to concentrate on the coalitions with respect to the customers, other manufacturers, and the organism.

The distinguishing feature of concomitant coalitions is that the coalitions are entered into *simultaneously with and against the same players*. Thus, the organism enters into a coalition with the customers, and against other manufacturers, offering to sell directly to the customers. Simultaneously, the organism enters into coalition with other manufacturers against the customers, offering to sell to the customers via other manufacturers. Here the organism enters into coalitions with and against the same party. Similarly, other manufacturers enter into coalitions with the organism against the customers; and simultaneously with the customers against the organism. So also, customers enter into coalitions with other manufacturers against the organism; and with the organism against other manufacturers.

What new policy insights do concomitant coalitions offer?

CONCOMITANT COALITIONS: RESALE I, RESALE II

ORGANISM VIS-À-VIS DISTRIBUTORS

The basic question before the organism is: How should the organism act vis-à-vis its distributors? The organism may enter into coalitions with the customers, and bid to supplant the distributors. It may negotiate with other manufacturers to supply the distributor customers, thus saving warehousing costs. So can the customers collude among themselves with other manufacturers, etc.

Freight costs, as observed earlier, often make the difference between profit and loss. Under existing arrangements, shipments are made from Plant D. Distributor F acts as Carrier C to make part of the shipment possible. Distributor F also sells the remaining part of the shipments in his capacity as a distributor.

Alternative to shipments via Distributor F, Distributor G could be employed as transportation agent by the organism. Should the organism decide to dispense with Distributors F and G, it could seek another distributor, or group of distributors, acting also as transportation agents, failing which the organism should be prepared to make the shipments to the customers itself from Plants A, B, and C.[3]

---

[3] George K. Chacko, *op. cit.,* pp. 815 - 816.

UTILITIES OF PLAYERS

What are the "utilities" of the players?

To the distributor, it is the net profit from Resale I and Resale II, coupled with backhaul revenue. Resale I is the most profitable transaction of the distributor with the organism; therefore, the net profit from Resale I could be considered the highest rate of return for the distributor. On the basis of the net profit to the distributor from Resale I, net profit from Resale II was computed. In addition, the revenue obtained by the distributor by acting as carriers for other organisms en route to the organism's Plant D was added to resale revenues I and II to give the total net revenue.

For the organism, the "utility" measure consists of the *net profit equivalent*. The available accounting data provided revenue from sales for the period under consideration. From this, freight and handling were subtracted to derive the net sales. Net sales revenue minus the statistically determined unit variable cost gave the net profit equivalent, which reflected a cost element in terms of unused capacity, based on empirical data. The measure provided a reasonably valid criterion of fixed and variable costs that could be reconciled with experienced judgment. In order to study the different moves and their associated outcome for the organism, the products were divided into two groups, with output as the independent variable, and cost the dependent variable. Least-square analysis of 52-month data yielded multiple-regression coefficients, providing fixed and variable costs used in the determination of profit equivalent.

Net profit equivalent provided for the possibility of *loss* when merely the sales volume was maintained or even increased. The organismic objective was thus changed from more volume to more profits.

CONCOMITANT COALITIONS: (a) PRESENT RESALE I TRANSACTIONS

As a result of the attention given to net profit equivalent of the organism as the objective, instead of volume sales, a new policy direction emerged. It was not essential to sell to all the distributor customers; it would be adequate if some of the customers could be persuaded to buy directly from the organism, instead of indirectly through the distributors, the exact requisite customer composition being a function of the net profit equivalent.

In order to determine the required amount of sales to customers to maintain the net profit equivalent disposition of the organism, the freight costs involved in supplying the customers from plants A, B, and C, instead of Plant D, has to be ascertained. What is the cost of shipments to customers by other distributors, by other manufacturers, or by means of other transportation agents? To calculate alternative freight costs, the geographic distribution of customers with respect to Plant D during a recent period was determined from actual data. Representative points were identified 100 miles, 200 miles, 300 miles, etc., from Plant D. The *least favorable freight costs* were determined for direct shipment from Plant B to the customer collections within cells 100 miles, 101–200 miles, 201–300 miles, etc. Tangents were drawn from Plant B to the concentric circles drawn with Plant D as center and radius, multiples of 100 miles. The farthest point on the concentric circle in the vicinity of the tangent was taken as the point to which shipments would be made (in order to avoid shipment to impassable mountains and lakes).

The *most favorable freight costs* were arrived at on the basis of actual shipments during a recent period. The shipments were assumed to be made from Plant A via Carrier A, from Plant B via Carrier B, and from Plant C via Carrier C. The least-cost freight combination was determined from among the three, on the basis of unrestricted source of supply and means of transportation.

Thus, it was possible to calculate the freight costs of the organism under both the most favorable and the least favorable freight arrangements. Status quo freight calculations were made from the original invoices themselves so the actual costs of shipments were also available.

What does freight do to the profit picture? As shipments are made from Plant B per least favorable freight to and from Warehouse A, it represents a net loss to the organism. It will be more profitable for the organism to forsake the business involved.

However, there are two other possible freight rates, both of which are favorable to the organism. On the basis of actual shipment rates available for the recent period, to and from Warehouse A, the freight costs for shipment from Plant B yield a net profit instead of net loss. If shipments are made directly from Plant B, without the use of Warehouse A, still additional net profits are indicated.[4]

On this basis, it was found that the status quo net profit equivalent of the organism could be maintained with only 49.5 percent of the net profit equivalent obtainable when shipments are made from Plant B *directly to the customers*. Similarly, 38.6 percent of the net profit equivalent obtainable from direct shipments from Plant C also provided status quo net profit equivalent.

, [4] George K. Chacko, *op. cit.*, pp. 816 - 817.

Looking at the situation in another way, if customers contributing 49.5 percent of the net profit equivalent are maintained when shipments are made from Plant B directly, the organism is no worse off than when it operated through the distributors. In other words, if there is a probability of 0.495 that the customers under the distributor system will be maintained under direct shipment from Plant B, then the organism can maintain its net profit equivalent under status quo. Thus, if the organism can associate probability value of 0.495 with the event, it would permit the organism seriously to bargain with the distributors, from a position of independence with respect to them.

We see from Table XX that if Resale I Customers C_6 and C_7, both of Distributor G, and Resale I Customers C_5 and C_1, both of Distributor F, are maintained as customers when the organism ships outputs directly to them, it would provide the organism with a position of independence with respect to distributors in Resale I operations.

CONCOMITANT COALITION: (b) RESALE II TRANSACTIONS

Resale II transactions relate to product volumes higher than Resale I transactions — for Distributor F, Resale II transactions are 1.92 times the Resale I transactions, and for Distributor G, 2.30 times.

Should shipments from Plant C of another manufacturer not be

TABLE XX

RESALE I TRANSACTIONS: STATUS QUO NET PROFIT
EQUIVALENTS UNDER DIFFERENT SHIPMENT ALTERNATIVES

Shipments from	Required probability of customer survival for maintenance of status quo net profit equivalent	Minimum group of customers who can provide the required probability
Distributor F's Customer Clientele[a]		
Plant C	0.386	C_5 or C_1 and C_2
Plant A	0.723	C_5 and C_2
Plant B.2	0.659	C_5 and C_2
Plant B.3	0.495	C_5 and C_1 or C_4
Distributor G's Customer Clientele[b]		
Plant C	0.700	C_6
Plant A	1.442	
Plant B.2	1.291	
Plant B.3	0.925	C_6, C_7

[a] Contribution to total Resale I: Customer $C_1 = 11.8$, Customer $C_2 = 29.0$, Customer $C_3 = 4.7$, Customer $C_4 = 11.8$, Customer $C_5 = 42.7$; total $= 100.0$ percent.

[b] Contribution to total Resale I: Customer $C_6 = 66.7$, Customer $C_7 = 33.3$; Total $= 100.0$ percent.

Source: George K. Chacko, "Bargaining Strategy in a Production and Distribution Problem," *Operations Research* (November–December, 1961), p. 818.

possible, the organism can threaten to ship directly from Plant B. In order for these production alternatives to be effective, the minimum number of customers who need to be maintained under direct shipment arrangements with the organism are as follows:

Shipment from	Resale I	Resale II
Plant C	C_5	C_8, C_9, C_{10}, C_{11}, C_{12}, and C_{13}
Plant B.3	C_5 and C_1	C_8, C_9, C_{10}, C_{12}, C_{13}, C_{14}, C_{15}, C_{16} *plus* customers representing 2.5 percent of total Resale II

We represent in Table XXI the minimum group of customers who can provide the required probability of assuring net profit equivalence to the organism. A strategically advantageous move for the organism is: (1) Shipment arrangements with Plant C (other manufacturer), (2) Maintenance of Customer C_5 for Resale I of Distributor F, and (3) Maintenance of Customer C_8 through C_{13} for his Resale II.

IMPUTATIONS IN CONCOMITANT COALITIONS

In the preceding discussion a bargaining position of great strength was found to be available to the business organization, enabling it to convert what was asserted to be a net loss position into one of net profit, when concomitant coalitions based on self-interest were explored. The coalitions involved the organism and outside players.

The same principle of opposing alignment can be applied to the organism itself, analytically split into two, e.g., the long-term interests of the organism on the one hand and the short-term profits on the other. The organism can be a nation, for instance, contemplating entry into a common market. In this instance, unlike in the business situation discussed previously, the creation of a value of the game is contingent upon the fact of the game itself. In order to appreciate the implications of this observation, let us consider coalitions and imputations in general.

Coalitions presuppose: (1) parallelism of interests, (2) probability of increased payoff by acting in concert, (3) the source of improved payoff being the remaining players in the game, playing individually or in concert; and (4) the process of splitting the improved values of the game being mutually acceptable.

Thus, if A, B, and C can each obtain the value of 10 units in a game, A and B may decide to act in concert against C, if and only if A and B can together obtain more than 20 units as the value of the game. The upper limit of the increased payoff is 10 units, which, in this instance, would be taken away from C. A and B have to agree to the process of splitting this extra 10 units which they have a probability of winning if they act in concert, but do not have any probability of winning if they play by themselves.

But the increased payoff is only a *probability*: It is not certain that A and B will in fact get the additional units from C. C may suggest to A

TABLE XXI

RESALE II TRANSACTIONS: STATUS QUO NET PROFIT
EQUIVALENTS UNDER DIFFERENT SHIPMENT ALTERNATIVES

Shipments from	Required probability of customers survival for maintenance of status quo net profit equivalent	Minimum group of customers who can provide the required probability
Distributor F's Customer Clientele[a]		
Plant C	0.386	$C_8, C_9, C_{10}, C_{11}, C_{12}, C_{13}$
Plant A	0.723	
Plant B.2	0.659	
Plant B.3	0.495	$C_8, C_9, C_{10}, C_{11}, C_{12}, C_{13},$ $C_{14}, C_{15}, C_{16}.$ *plus* customers representing 2.5% of total resale
Distributor G's Customer Clientele[b]		
Plant C	0.700	
Plant A	1.442	
Plant B.2	1.291	
Plant B.3	0.925	

[a]Contribution to Total Resale II		[b]Contribution to Total Resale II	
Customer C_8	14.2%	Customer C_{17}	5.2%
Customer C_9	9.1	Customer C_{18}	5.2
Customer C_{10}	6.4	Customer C_{19}	3.9
Customer C_{11}	3.8	Customer C_{20}	7.9
Customer C_{12}	3.2	Customer C_{21}	2.0
Customer C_{13}	2.8	Customer C_{22}	2.0
	39.5%	Customer C_{23}	2.0
Customer C_{14}	2.5	Customer C_{24}	1.7
Customer C_{15}	2.5	Customer C_{25}	1.3
Customer C_{16}	2.5	Customer C_{26}	1.3
	47.0%	Customer C_{27}	0.7
			33.2%
Transient Customers	53.0	Transient Customers	66.8
	100.0%		100.0%

Source: George K. Chacko, "Bargaining Strategy in a Production and Distribution Problem," *Operations Research* (November–December, 1961), p. 823.

that A and C could act in concert and bid for the 10 additional units of gain from B. Similarly, C could suggest to B that B and C, acting in concert, could bid to obtain additional payoffs from A. Which of the three possible groupings, namely (i) A and B against C, (ii) A and C against B, and (iii) B and C against A materializes, depends upon the probability of improved earnings, and the process of sharing such earnings. The three players may very well decide to act by themselves, and be content with the 10 units each that they have a much greater degree of certainty of obtaining as individual players, acting by themselves.

Suppose we have a zero-sum three person game in which any coalition of any two players can extract one unit of value from the third player. Then writing $v(s)$ for the value of the characteristic function of the subset of players S, we have

$$v(0) = 0$$
$$v(1) = v(2) = (3) = -1$$
$$v(1, 2) = v(2, 3) = v(1, 3) = 1$$
$$v(1, 2, 3) = 0$$

$v(1,2,3)$ means the value of a play to the coalition of players 1, 2, and 3. In such a game a coalition is bound to be formed, since only in that way can a player protect himself from loss. Then comes the question of remuneration for the actual gain from coalitions. Suppose player A wants to retain x under all conditions. Then either of the partners of coalition can hope to get only $(1 - x)$ in a coalition if A succeeded in retaining x. . . .

The authors, John von Neumann and Oskar Morgenstern, show that the formation of a coalition depends on a feature of the game, in the case $v(1,2) + v(1,3) + v(2,3) > 0$. This enables the game to be divided into inessential (i.e., games in which coalitions do not pay) and (essential) those in which coalitions do. Coalitions will always be formed in such (essential) games in the absence of rules forbidding them.

The value of the play to each player in the above game can be written down for each possible coalition thus:

		Player	
Coalition	1	2	3
(1, 2)	½	½	–1
(1, 3)	½	–1	½
(2, 3)	–1	½	½

Each row of this table is called an imputation, which is simply a set of numbers showing the distribution of the total gain among the players. The whole table is called a *solution* since it shows all the ways in which a game can be played consistently with the rational behavior on the part of the players. No imputation of a solution dominates over any other one of the set of imputations of the solution, and at least some of them dominate over imputations of the other set.

One imputation is said to dominate over another if the members of a subset of players do better under the dominant imputation than under the dominated one and if the amount going to subset is no greater than v (s) the amount they are able to ensure themselves by the formation of a coalition.[5]

Both of these are zero-sum games. The *gain* of the coalition of A and B, 10 units, is exactly the *loss* of C. But when the sum is not zero then complications arise. If there is a bonus that can be obtained only by A, B, and C finishing the game, then, that bonus is not a result of the individual player's roles in the game, but of the organismic nature of the game as a whole. *In other words, A, B, and C are doing themselves a definite favor by playing the game: at the end there is a bonus which is available to all the three, and which is available only at the end of the game and not before.*

Suppose this bonus is a booby prize. The attractiveness of the bonus will be much less than if the bonus were, say, $1,000,000.

Now suppose that there is a bonus promised at the completion of the game, but whether the bonus is $1,000,000 in cash or a booby prize is not known. In this instance, the players will have to go by the probabilities with which they think the $1,000,000 bonus or the booby prize will materialize, in deciding whether or not to play the game. They can still play the game each as an individual player; or two of them in concert, i.e., as a *coalition* against the third.

IMPUTATIONS IN CONCOMITANT COALITIONS: EMPIRICAL ILLUSTRATIONS

COAL COMMUNITY, COMMON MARKET

The European Coal Community, the Inner Six and the Outer Seven, and later the European Common Market — are all instances of nonzero sum games. The nature of the bonus of these games was not predetermined: there were only probabilities. *With* the tariff barriers, preventing the free flow of goods between national territories, the players, in this case the national economies, could generally be sure about the earnings that they would get from the tariffs imposed upon the commodities, since minimum quantities of these were indispensable for consumption in the

---

[5] K. George Chacko, "Economic Behaviour — a New Theory," *Indian Journal of Economics,* Vol. XXX (April, 1950), pp. 353-354.

respective countries. *Without* the tariffs, the game in which coal and steel would flow freely across existing national territories, the bonus would take the form of a greater demand for coal and steel; which would result in larger earnings for the producers and larger sources of energy for the consumers. However, it was also likely that the respective countries may have lived on the minimal basic requirements of coal and steel for such a long time that, like the underwater fish which lose the power of their eyes owing to disuse for sustained periods, they might have settled to an undernourishment equilibrium. If this were so, the lifting of the tariff barriers would not lead to any better level of production and sales activity. *Same sales, no tariffs.*

These considerations apply on a large scale to the European Common Market. Prior to the game of Common Market, the player countries obtained revenues from tariffs imposed on the flow of goods and services across their territories. When these were to be substantially lifted, the decline in the tariffs had to be offset by: (1) increased flow of goods and services across the national boundaries, resulting from a tremendously larger market for these goods and services, (2) advantages of division of labor, both realized and enhanced by means of the larger area from which to draw the resources required. In this process it is almost inevitable that the crutches provided by the tariffs to "infant industries" within different countries would no longer be available; and faced with the competition from "adult industries" from other members of the Common Market, the local industries would decline, and perhaps die. By the same token, some of the local industries would flourish, because the local availability of resources confers special advantages over all other countries of the Common Market. Thus, the assessment of the probability of bonus or booby prize will depend on the probable course of prosperity and depression in different segments of the national economy. These are no certainties: therefore, decisions have to be made in advance, and in partial ignorance of the outcome.

Parallel to the bonus in the game situation would be the increased economic prosperity of the countries which unite in the Common Market effort.

Even if some of the countries would receive relative booby prizes, they also share in the bonus which can be obtained *only if* adequate number of countries play in the game of the Common Market. Here again, the bonus of economic prosperity, arising out of increased employment, increased incomes, increased expenditures, and increased well-being — are no certainty, they are only probabilities.

CURRENT RESEARCH EFFORTS (A) AND FUTURE RESEARCH EFFORTS (B)

Current vs. future research efforts provides an intriguing instance of concomitant coalition. The very furtherance of understanding it accomplishes almost insures that the accomplishments themselves will be supplanted by efforts to generate further accomplishments. Thus the current research efforts (A) themselves contain the seeds of future research efforts (B), so that the current research efforts may be considered at work to obliterate themselves: a game in which A plays against B and simultaneously with B against itself, A.

We may characterize the opposing interests of current research efforts by alter ego and anti-ego. As we designated current research efforts by A, we may abbreviate alter ego of current efforts by A-ALT and the anti-ego of current efforts by A-ANT. The opposition of interests here stems from the juxtaposition of A with B, which together constitute research efforts (R). In this case the organism's research effort is "bigger than the both of" A and B.

What are the consequences of R being bigger than A and B combined? By R we mean the entire stream of man's efforts to extend his control over environment through discovery of patterns in elemental relationships so that they can be manipulated at different levels for different purposes. Included in it is the theoretical work on nuclear structure of matter as well as the laboratory efforts to relieve headache.

The organismic nature of research efforts (R) assumes a separate existence of its own: an existence in which the step-by-step successes in diverse fields precipitate from time to time quantum jumps in the behavioral properties of resources. These quantum jumps do not occur in prespecified segments of R, e.g., seventh day of the seventh month at seven o'clock in the morning. When and where such quantum jumps will occur is uncertain, but whether such quantum jumps will occur is not uncertain. Neither the origin of such quantum jumps, nor the radiating impact of such jumps can be forecast with any great degree of accuracy. However, even as an elephant does not walk into the clutches of the sleeping lion, if there is no research, then we can safely state that there will be no quantum jumps. The highly attractive value of the bonus in the form of quantum jumps tends to overshadow the booby prize value of bonuses in the form of mere academic, linear extensions of behavioral properties of resources.

There is no way of legislating that bonuses only shall be obtained, or that bonuses shall be obtained at particular times. By the same token, legislation is ineffective with respect to the yield of booby prizes — their nature and magnitude. The only course of action open is to continue research efforts and take booby prizes and bonuses as they come.

Once the inescapability of the need for research efforts is granted, irrespective of the field, the tactical objectives (page 34) will be linear extension of behavioral properties of resources, and strategic objectives (page 32) will be quantum jumps in the behavioral properties of resources. Current research efforts (A) are in the realm of tactical objectives, and not strategic objectives. As the name indicates, there is no direct, linear, progression from linear extensions to quantum jumps; scores of hundreds of linear extensions may be necessary for a quantum jump, but none of them is sufficient. But the very same decision to conduct current research spells disaster to the survival objective of current research efforts.

The innovation profile is constructed on the basis of quantum jumps in the behavioral properties of resources of the organism, the tempo of innovation of the organism, and the tempo of innovation of the competition. The intent here is to change, and, hopefully, change for the better. Change involves replacement of the past by the present, and the present by the future. The judicious allocation of resources for research and development are predicated on the premise that dimensions of discovery and tempo of innovation can be engineered to yield a suitable new lift to the output portfolio of the organism.

But there is an escalatory procedure underneath the improvements and innovations and outputs. If one walks up an escalator, the immediately obvious progress can be stated in terms of the steps climbed. But even as the person is climbing the steps, the escalator itself is moving in the same direction. Therefore, using the handrails of the escalator as the frame of reference, the escalatory motion accentuates the ambulatory motion of the person.

Something like this takes place in the process of discovery associated with research efforts. The dimensions of discovery and the tempo of innovation are somewhat like the steps on the escalator which are directly visible, and which are climbed step-by-step. However, the very process of step-by-step climbing of making improvements in the performance of current properties of resources, or of making innovations, leads to a deeper understanding of the appropriate underlying structure of matter, or its conversion into energy. Such basic understandings contribute, on occasion, to an altogether radical departure in the step-by-step climbing with respect to behavioral properties of resources. Even as the effort of escalatory movement is not apparent until the top of the stairs is reached, so also the effect of radical departures that have been generated by the escalatory movement of fundamental understanding do not come to ready recognition except at discrete time intervals. Unlike the escalator, however, the specific instant at which the escalatory movement will be clearly recognized is not predetermined. In terms of the calendar, it may be months, it may be weeks, it may be years, it may be days within which such a discovery is made, with reverberations in all directions.

Thus, the current research efforts to develop photographic techniques yielding black-and-white pictures in 10 seconds contains the almost certain extinction of research efforts on black-and-white pictures. For, it is conceptually clear that, should black-and-white pictures be made available in 10 seconds, so can pictures in color. If color pictures are available in 10 seconds, the demand for black-and-white is likely to be much less than if there were no quick color development of pictures in 10 seconds available. It is true that color photography development would follow a different orbit from that of black-and-white pictures. But it is also true that time will lag between 10-second black-and-white and 10-second color photography. However, the feasibility of instantaneous color development is imbedded in the development of instantaneous photography itself. Therefore, one cannot unequivocally affirm that research efforts on black-and-white shall continue in their present form indefinitely. The only feasible decision is that there will be current efforts on black-and-white. These current research efforts will be supplanted by future research efforts, whose objective may no longer be black-and-white photography.

CONFLICTING OBJECTIVES AND CONFLICTING CHOICES

The Table XXII, this antithesis of *current* research efforts (A) and *future* research efforts (B) is shown to be similar to the conflict of individual interests of members of the European Coal and Steel Community vis-à-vis the Community, and members of the European Common Market vis-à-vis the Market as a whole. In entering into the European Coal and Steel Community, a country stands to lose tariffs that it derived because there was no Coal and Steel Community. On the other hand, there are the prospects of increased sales revenue, which will not be available without the Community. The objectives of the alter ego of the country, namely that the country's economy should surpass present performance, and that of the anti-ego of the country, namely, that income from tariffs should continue, lead to conflicting choices: sacrifice the tariffs of the country to support the community, or sacrifice the idea of the community to insure the continuance of tariff revenue. These choices are not coexistent: they are mutually exclusive. However, it is the organismic relationship into which the country

TABLE XXII

CONCOMITANT COALITIONS IN CUSTOMS UNION

GAME	PLAYERS	PLAYER ORGANISM	COALITION MEMBERS	PAYOFF Gain
European Coal and Steel Community	Country X: Alter ego (X-ALT), Other Countries (Y) : Anti-ego (X-ANT)	Coal Community (Z)	FOR: X-ALT, Y	X: P_1 (Increased Sales Revenue)
				Y: P_2 (Increased Sales Revenue)
				Z: P_3 (Freer flow of More goods and services)
			AGAINST: X-ANT	
European Common Market	Country M: Alter ego (M-ALT), Other Countries (M) : Anti-ego (M-ANT)	Common Market (Q)	FOR: M-ALT, N	M: P_5 (New Adult Industry, Improved Adult Industry)
				N: P_6 (New Adult Industry, Improved Adult Industry)
				Q: P_7 (General Higher Standard of Living)
			AGAINST: M-ANT	
Research Efforts Allocations	Current Efforts A: Alter ego (A-ALT), Future Efforts (B), Anti-ego (A-ANT)	Research Efforts (R)	FOR: A-ALT, B	A: P_9 (Linear Extension of Behavioral Properties)
				B: P_{10} (Linear Extension of Behavioral Properties)
				R: P_{11} (Quantum Jump(s) in Behavioral Properties)
			AGAINST: A-ANT	

CONSIDERATIONS AND RESEARCH EFFORTS ALLOCATIONS

	PAYOFF		Player	CONFLICTING OBJECTIVES		CONFLICTING CHOICES	
Illustrative Probability	Loss	Illustrative Probability		Survive	Surpass	Sacrifice	Support
0.0–0.4			X-ALT		X economy should surpass present performance	Sacrifice X to	Support Z
0.1–0.6							
0.5–0.7							
	P₄ (No Tariffs)	0.8–0.9	X-ANT	Tariffs Should Survive		Sacrifice Z to	Support X
0.0–0.4			M-ALT		M resources should surpass current levels of employment	Sacrifice M to	Support Q
0.1–0.6							
0.5–0.7							
	P₈ (No Infant Industry)	0.8–0.9	M-ANT	Infant Industry Should Survive		Sacrifice Q to	Support M
0.0–0.4			A-ALT		Organism should surpass current level of outputs	Sacrifice A to	Support R
0.1–0.6							
0.5–0.7							
	P₁₂ (No Further Allocations)	0.8–0.9	A-ANT	Current Research Efforts Should Survive		Sacrifice R to	Support A

enters that brings about the conflicting choices. Should the country seek to save its tariffs and lose itself? Or seek to lose itself in the community, and thus save itself?

It is this dilemma which sets the stage for concomitant coalitions. The country enters into coalitions with other countries to form the Community, by which action it is aligning itself against and with itself — *against* because the country which enters into the coalition to form the organism loses its original identity; and *for* because the broader range of economic integration beyond those of tariffs and trade may both form and foster industries.

If the country does not enter the Common Market, it preserves its status quo ante; so also the country which does not enter the Coal and Steel Community. But in both instances the country by playing for itself is really acting against its best interests.

In the case of the country considering entry into the Coal and Steel Community or the Common Market, the physical survival of the player-in-terest is nearly certain: there will be a Luxembourg recognizable as Luxembourg even if the Common Market commerce lines criss-cross the country. However, in the case of current research efforts, the current is inevitably going to be replaced by the future: and there will be no current research physically surviving as such. Should the organism be persuaded (perhaps by the research component) to try to prolong the physical survival of present pet projects, the research component can be directed not to perform effectively, and deliberately not to make any significant contributions to the present pet projects. Or, the organism can decide not to undertake the pet projects at all, lest by the very act of making them current research efforts they invite the march of time to sweep them under.

In other words, technique of instantaneous snapshot development may be not researched upon at all. Or, if it is inevitable that some research on black-and-white instantaneous snapshot development must be undertaken, then the researchers can deliberately drag their feet on the job, and refuse to uncover any method of perfecting it. Counteracting both these tendencies is the institution of free enterprise. If Organism A chooses either not to engage in current research efforts, or to choke the useful yield from current research efforts, then by that very process organism A is letting the leadership in instantaneous snapshot development possibility slip to Organism B.

Thus the question is not to do or not to do research, but how to do research. It is futile to waste resources on a "show" of research, deliberately withholding any ideas from coming to fruition. Even when ideas do come to fruition, marketing considerations may delay their implementation: even if color photography methods are perfected, it is likely that marketing considerations would lead to the introduction of the color film into the market after the lapse of a certain amount of time. Even after the color films are introduced into the market, both black-and-white and color films will continue. In instances of keener competition, radio survived television after initial impact and vacillation; so has the movie industry survived television. When a method of producing aluminum was discovered, it was feared that steel might go out of style; but both have managed to develop their own soaring markets.

In allocating funds to research and development, the time dimension offers fresh insights into the allocation of resources to research and development. Periodic Table of Product Diversification (PTPD) performance indicates the need for preventive investment in order to maintain the performance leadership of the organism in its field and to improve it. Satisfaction of this need is circumscribed by the dimensions of discovery and the tempo of innovation. Even when the technometric structure permits plotting the locus of realization, the tempo of innovation of the organism will determine how far and how fast the inherent sequencing involved in the transformation of the idea into output shall progress. While these influences are primarily organism-oriented, the time dimension introduces *non-organism-oriented changes* that are inevitable if current research efforts are undertaken. If PTPD indicates that the organism should run in order to keep still, the time dimension indicates that when it runs, it may find itself flying, instead of standing still. How well this fact is appreciated by the organism in its allocation of funds to research and development will decide whether the influence of time dimension is like riding the tail of a tiger, or like taking at the flood the tide in the affairs of men, which leads to fortune.

CHAPTER EIGHT

COMMITTING TODAY'S RESOURCES TO TOMORROW'S HOPES

The plans for the air defence of Great Britain had, as early as the autumn of 1937, been rewritten round the assumption that the promises made by our scientists for the *still unproven radar* would be kept [italics supplied].[1]

Thus Winston Churchill committed, to a large measure, his hopes for British defense upon "promises [of] the still unproven radar." The unborn morrow wrapped up in the unproven radar was virtually the scientific hinge of fate on which the destiny of the British Empire hung, radar to which the precious but limited resources of the day were committed on the "assumption that the promise . . . would be kept."

---

[1] Winston S. Churchill, *The Grand Alliance* (Boston; Houghton Mifflin Company, 1951), p. 45.

As in Churchill's day, our own resources have to be committed to tomorrow's hopes on the "assumption that the promises . . . would be kept." Since it cannot be legislated that promises shall be kept, and since survival is at stake and resources are not unlimited, we can have no guarantees of success in our effort. However, we may improve our chance of success by learning intelligently. And this process of learning intelligently is as much apropos to realizing the promises of space conquest as to survival on the terra firma.

EXPLOSIVE MUSHROOMING OF INTERACTIONS

> "Outer space is the new frontier: research and exploration will have profound and revolutionary effects on our economic growth." In a survey made in 1960 of 1,950 leaders of U.S. industry, the *Harvard Business Review* found that 85% of the executives agreed with the [foregoing] proposition. The same men went on to predict that nonspace benefits from the program might include "revolutionary improvements" in communications, medical and biological knowledge, weather forecasting, electronic devices, better computers, new structural materials, etc. In a follow-up survey made last year, a similar group indicated that business optimism was still high. And almost three-quarters of the executives who were asked, replied that they believed the program would also develop "new products for our everyday lives" — a possibility not mentioned in the earlier survey.[2]

This outreach into outer space is over almost uncharted territory. Neither the objects of conquest of space nor the means to achieve them are clearly or uniquely determined. In fact, it is quite likely that conquests will unfold further territories to conquer; and the success of the means employed will open up newer and possibly more efficient means of conquest of space.

CHALLENGES, CHOICES, AND INTERACTIONS

Consider the challenges of distance. Distance can be traversed quickly via speedier means of transport, or via shorter routes. One challenge, two choices.

Or consider the challenge of space. Space can be apprehended via bigger boosters which can travel farther and endure longer, or via more effective payloads. One challenge, two choices.

These choices are independent. Thus, speedier means of transport

---

2 John Dille, "The Revolution Isn't Coming — It Is Already Here," *Life* (Sept. 25, 1964), p. 1027.

as well as shorter routes can be employed simultaneously to annhilate distance; so can bigger boosters and better payloads for space conquest, two challenges, four choices: or 2 × 2 interactions between challenges and choices.

Consider the challenge of travel not in space but on earth. The travel can be by land, water, or air — or a combination of all the three. On the land, horse-and-buggy, automobiles, and trains are alternate means of transport. As new places are discovered, and as the population increases, the demand for the use of the means of transport by land increases rapidly, so rapidly as to outstrip the capability of the entire means of transport on wheels. The transition from transports on slower wheels to faster wheels is, in terms of Chapter 3 terminology, linear extensions of behavioral properties. However, when wings are introduced into transportation, the transition from wheels to wings is a quantum jump. In Chapter 4 the choices of subsonic and supersonic transports are shown as two types of improvement in the use of air as a means of travel; to which we may add transonic as a third choice.

Thus, corresponding to the challenge of travel on earth, we have land, air, and water transports; and corresponding to the challenge of travel by land, we have horse-and-buggy, automobiles, and trains; and corresponding to the challenge of travel by air, we have subsonic, transonic, and supersonic transports. In other words, corresponding to the two challenges of travel by land or air, we have six choices, not to mention the choices of water transport.

In determining how we should invest research efforts into travel by land and by air, both of which can be complementary means to fulfill the needs of travel, we have 2 × 3, or 6 interactions to consider. Admittedly, these choices are macro-choices, subsonic choices alone comprising mono-planes, double-engine planes, four-engine planes, etc., not to speak of all the different brands of vehicles in each category. The point is that in meeting the challenges of today, we have choices of tomorrow, the *interaction* between challenges and choices growing at a more rapid rate than either the challenges or the choices alone.

The rapidity of the growth of the choices is a function of the growth of human knowledge itself.

> There is adequate evidence that knowledge in the physical sciences has been growing at an exponential rate since 1700 . . . doubling [every] fifteen years . . .
>
> The number of choices available to the [aircraft] designer in 1935 . . . were on the order of two major choices. In 1955 there were more than 360 choices available.

> If we assume that the number of technical choices is proportional, *on the average,* to the amount of physical knowledge, one can hypothesize that the upper limit of the number of choices available to weapons designers will be a gamma or factorial function of the amount of knowledge existing at a particular time. If we then arbitrarily establish this relation for design of an aircraft weapons system as two in 1935, *in conformity with the estimated situation,* i.e., so that the number of choices is equal to some function of the knowledge existing in the physical sciences, then we can calculate the number of choices equal to fractorial *N,* where *N* doubles every fifteen years as a function of time. . . . [Italics supplied.][3]

When we take into account not only the explosive growth in choices available owing to the developments in human knowledge, but also in newer challenges which man decides to accept (Space has been there for millions of years, but only in the last few years did man accept the challenge of space because he did not have the wherewithal of technical know-how), the growth in human knowledge itself opening up new vistas for man to conquer, the interaction between the challenges and the choices mushrooms explosively. In Table XXIII this explosive mushrooming is illustrated.

INHERENT SEQUENCING: IDEA TO OUTPUT

While the interactions mushroom, certain limitations are imposed on effective use of these developments. This inherent delay is common to all enterprises, large and small, public as well as private.

> Now let us assume that the Soviet Union decided on a particular weapons system in 1955. At that time there were about 200 choices available. Let us assume it is 1957 before we become aware in a somewhat uncertain way of the probable characteristics of the forthcoming Soviet weapons system, scheduled by them to become fully operational in 1960. . . .
> The Soviet weapon system, which becomes operational in 1960, will have been phased out sometime between 1965 and 1967 and will have been replaced by a *new* weapons system based upon the technology of about 1960 to 1962 when some 5,000 choices have become available (although choices too will obsolesce). The U.S. defensive technology of 1957, with some 500 choices available, will thus come into being after the Soviet attack system that it was designed to counter is superseded by a superior Soviet attack system.[4]

---

[3] Ellis A. Johnson, "The Crisis in Science and Technology and Its Effects on Military Development," *Operations Research* (January – February, 1958), pp. 14, 16 - 17.

[4] *Ibid.,* p. 19.

While Ellis Johnson here considers only the multiplicity of choices, it is essential that we take interactions between challenge and choice also into account. Thus, if 1955 is t_0 in Table XXIII, 1962 would be t_7, the illustrative interactions considered by the Soviet Union being respectively 2 and 600,000. The U.S. selection in 1957, t_2, would have had an interaction of only 250 to choose from. A weapons system built effectively from 250 interaction situation would be considerably superior to one built equally effectively from only 2 interactions, but would be inadequate to meet the challenges of a weapons system based on the effective use of 600,000 interactions.

TABLE XXIII

EXPLOSIVE MUSHROOMING OF INTERACTIONS BETWEEN
CHALLENGES AND CHOICES — ILLUSTRATIVE

TIME	CHALLENGE	CHOICES	INTERACTION
t_0	1	2	2
t_1	3	5	15
t_2	10	25	250
t_3	18	60	1,080
t_4	40	150	6,000
t_5	60	400	24,000
t_6	120	1,000	120,000
t_7	300	2,000	600,000
t_8	480	6,000	2,880,000
t_9	700	10,000	7,000,000
t_{10}	1,000	15,000	15,000,000
t_{11}	3,000	20,000	60,000,000
t_{12}	9,000	30,000	270,000,000

However, the constraints imposed on effective selection comes from; (1) intelligence delay; (2) decision to respond; and (3) time for construction, to mention a few, which are inherent in any transformation of ideas into outputs. Even if we had *instantaneous* intelligence of Soviet intentions on new weapons systems, there are still many inevitable steps which have to be traveled before decisions can be made, and having made, outputs constructed; and having constructed, checked out; and having checked out, installed; and having installed, fully implemented. And during the progress of these steps, time marches on, making available an even larger array of challenges and choices, and even larger array of interactions which are bound to make obsolete the most modern constructions!

On a smaller scale, the dilemma of anticipation and response to technological advances applies to private enterprises. The interactions they have to choose from are necessarily smaller, limited both by the range of their interest and the limits of their funds. However, they have to invest today's resources for tomorrow's hopes, gambling not only on the promises of technology, but also on the disposition of the market.

INTELLIGENCE FROM CURRENT INFORMATION

This is where current information offers guidance. That tomorrow will be like today is perhaps too simple a hypothesis; but that tomorrow is another day is undeniable. If tomorrow is another day, any identification of tomorrow as reasonably belonging to a group of yesterdays, or a specifiably higher level than the group of yesterdays, would offer some guidance to committing today's resources. This is why we relate the nature and magnitude of the wants satisfied by the range of outputs yesterday and today, and assess the relative significance of the satisfaction the outputs have been able to offer. In addition to looking at the organism's own performance in the past and the present, current intelligence of competition's activity — present and potential — are germane to resource allocation decisions. We discussed in Chapter 5 the processing of information relating to the organism's performance; in Chapter 6 the processing of information relating to the performance of the competition.

WANTED: A METHODOLOGY OF LEARNING INTELLIGENTLY

In the face of mushrooming interactions between challenges and choices and inherent delays in implementing decisions, it is inevitable that errors be made in judgment.

> In Congressional testimony released yesterday, Defense Secretary Robert S. McNamara estimated that at least $1.2 billion was wasted on the abortive B-70 bomber project.
>
> The total cost of the project was $1.5 billion. . . .
>
> The question of how much of the money that was spent was really wasted came up when McNamara was asked whether what was learned from the B-70 work would not be of great value to other military and civilian projects, such as the supersonic transport.
>
> Here McNamara suggested that at least 80 per cent of the money was wasted.
>
> McNamara's general view has been that substantial "waste" of this sort is unavoidable in the defense program since it is rarely possible to know how valuable a development project is going to be before large sums have been spent.

The corollary to this, he has suggested, is that such waste has to be minimized by insisting on good evidence of probable value before big money is spent and even then by limiting spending as much as possible until the value of the project is proven.[5]

We have proposed in these pages that technological feasibility be systematically explored before choosing from among the different avenues of research, whether it be for national defense or for a new headache remedy. In order to choose effectively from among alternative allocation possibilities, it should be recognized that the decision-affecting and the decision-affected entities are organisms. Organismic viewpoint underlies operations research. It is the art of applying the scientific method to executive-type decision problems. It is also the practice of translating progressively what-can-be into what-is in industrial, commercial, military and/or institutional environments. Thus operations research is indispensable to identify the potentials of alternate solutions to meet the challenges of the environment as well as to implement them.

It is this organismic viewpoint which can effectively aid the selection from among alternatives, that line of action which holds the most promise of fulfillment of the organismic objectives, most of the time, in the long run.

---

[5] Howard Margolis, "Waste on B-70 Put at Billion by McNamara," *Washington Post* (May 15, 1965), p. A2.

INDEX

223